Insight
Science and Technology
For the Middle School
Revised Second Edition

CLASS VI

S. Basu Kasturi
Sardar Patel Vidyalaya
New Delhi

Anila Chadha
S.B.D.A.V. Public School
New Delhi

K. Kasinathan
Formerly Blue Bells School
New Delhi

S. Bhattacharya
Blue Bells School
New Delhi

OXFORD
UNIVERSITY PRESS

OXFORD
UNIVERSITY PRESS

YMCA Library Building, Jai Singh Road, New Delhi 110001

Oxford University Press is a department of the University of Oxford.
It furthers the University's objective of excellence in research, scholarship,
and education by publishing worldwide in

Oxford New York

Auckland Cape Town Dar es Salaam Hong Kong Karachi
Kuala Lumpur Madrid Melbourne Mexico City Nairobi
New Delhi Shanghai Taipei Toronto

With offices in

Argentina Austria Brazil Chile Czech Republic France Greece
Guatemala Hungary Italy Japan Poland Portugal Singapore
South Korea Switzerland Thailand Turkey Ukraine Vietnam

Oxford is a registered trade mark of Oxford University Press
in the UK and in certain other countries.

Published in India
by Oxford University Press

First published 1997
Eighth impression 2007

ISBN-13: 978-019-566717-2
ISBN-10: 0-19-566717-4

Typeset in Times New Roman
By Anvi Composers
Printed in India by Ram Book Binding, Delhi 110020
and published by Oxford University Press
YMCA Library Building, Jai Singh Road, New Delhi 110001

Preface

We are pleased to place before you the new, revised second edition of *Insight: Science and Technology* for class VI. The *Insight* series fully conforms to the latest guidelines and syllabi prescribed by the National Council of Educational Research and Training (NCERT) as also to those of all other major syllabi.

Science governs every aspect of our lives. Simple actions such as prying open the lid of a tin to phenomenal developments like artificial satellites, are all applications of science. As in the first edition, our attempt here is to kindle the interest of the young learner in the sciences. Thus, we have adopted an application-oriented approach to the subject. A number of activities simulating real-life situations are included in each chapter. Our aim is not only to inform but also to develop in young minds a scientific attitude towards life.

In this second edition we have reworked the chapters and provided the book with a new, attractive, reader-friendly layout. We have also increased the number and type of questions in each chapter to provide more practice to the learner.

This edition also includes the following student-friendly features:

- Each chapter begins with a list of topics covered in that chapter.

- Each topic is followed by *Recall* and *Let's Answer* to help reinforce the concepts studied.

- The *Activities* in a chapter enable students to understand the theory better with the aid of simple experiments.

- *Do You Know?* provides interesting chapter- or topic-related facts.

- The *Exercises* have been designed to test the student's conceptual grasp of the topics. Different methods of questioning such as Fill in the Blanks, Match the Following, etc. are included to make the exercises interesting for the student.

- *Think and Answer* questions are a special feature of the book. These questions require the student to apply the scientific principles studied to solve practical problems.

- *Teacher's Notes* recommends creative ways to approach a particular chapter or concept in the classroom.

We hope that both students and teachers will find this new edition appropriate and useful. We would consider our job done if this book is received with the same enthusiasm as was the first edition. Constructive criticism on any aspect of the series would be welcome.

The Authors

Contents

Contents

1

- Factors responsible for life on earth
- Structure of the earth
- Earth's atmosphere
- Oceans
- Water
- Soil
- Earth and the solar system

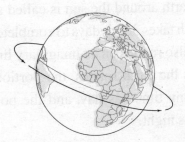

Our Earth

If you look at the sky at night, it looks like a big dark dome studded with numerous twinkling objects. You must have also noticed the moon and some other objects that do not twinkle. These are the planets. We live on one such planet—the earth. The human mind has always been curious about these heavenly bodies. *The branch of science that deals with the study of stars, planets and other heavenly bodies is called astronomy*. And a person who studies astronomy is an *astronomer*. The powerful tool they use is called a *telescope* (Fig. 1.1).

Fig. 1.1   Telescope

 Do You Know?

The unit for measuring distance in the universe is:

(i) Light year = Distance travelled by light in one year

1 light year = 9.460×10^{12} km

The brightest star, Sirius, is 8.7 light years away from the earth.

(ii) Parsec (pc)

1 pc = 3.26 light years

The planet earth is spherical in shape, flattened at the poles. It moves around the sun in a fixed elliptical path called the *orbit*. And this movement of the earth around the sun is called a *revolution*. The earth takes $365\frac{1}{4}$ days to complete one revolution. It also rotates on an imaginary line called the *axis*. As the earth rotates, the portion facing the sun at any time has day, and the portion facing away has night.

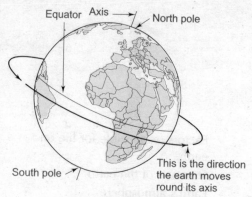

Equator Axis → North pole

South pole ↗

This is the direction the earth moves round its axis

Fig. 1.2   The earth

FACTORS RESPONSIBLE FOR LIFE ON EARTH

The following factors have helped life to originate and survive on earth:

(a) Right size and mass of the earth.

(b) Availability of water on earth.

(c) Ability of plants to prepare food using CO_2 from the atmosphere, nutrients from the soil, water, and sunlight.

(d) Right distance of the earth from the sun, so it has the right temperature range for life.

(e) Presence of air containing oxygen which is essential for life.

(f) An appropriate gravitational field which has helped the earth to hold on to its atmosphere and not allow gases such as O_2 (oxygen), CO_2 (carbon dioxide) or nitrogen to escape.

 Recall

- The study of heavenly bodies is called astronomy and the person who studies astronomy is called an astronomer.
- 1 light year = 9.46×10^{12} km
  1 parsec = 3.26 light years
- The movement of the earth, in a fixed orbit, around the sun is called a revolution.
- The earth rotates on an imaginary line called the axis. This rotation causes day and night.
- Right distance from the sun, appropriate gravitational field and the presence of important gases like oxygen are some of the factors responsible for life on earth.

Let's Answer

1. Name the planet closest to the earth.
2. What is the study of heavenly bodies called?
3. Who are astronomers? What is the name of the instrument they use?
4. Why is the earth considered the only planet in our solar system on which life can exist?

STRUCTURE OF THE EARTH

When earth was formed millions of years ago it was very hot. As time passed the surface of the earth cooled down and was separated into different layers. This reorganization of the earth into a layered state is known as *differentiation*. We find that the surface of the earth has different physical features such as mountains, hills, oceans, and plains. Similarly, there are three different layers of the earth (Fig. 1.3 and 1.4), namely, the crust, mantle and the core.

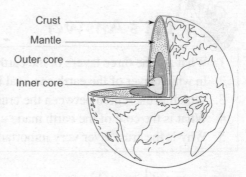

Fig. 1.3 Internal structure of the earth

The crust layer of the earth is very important as it is a rich source of metals such as iron, gold, fuels such as petrol and natural gas, etc. The materials from which these metals are obtained are called *minerals*.

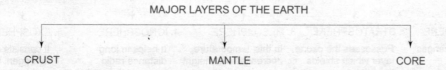

MAJOR LAYERS OF THE EARTH

CRUST	MANTLE	CORE
(i) Outermost layer of the earth.	(i) Region between the crust and the core.	(i) Innermost part of the earth.
(ii) Made up of lighter rocks rich in silica and aluminium.	(ii) Thickness is 2900 km below the crust.	(ii) It contains mostly iron and some metals like nickel and cobalt.
(iii) Thickness ranges from 35–60 km under the continents to 10 km under the oceans.	(iii) Consists of rocks made up of iron silicate and magnesium silicate.	(iii) It consists of an inner solid sphere surrounded by an outer fluid.
(iv) 71% of it is covered by oceans.	(iv) Under extreme temperature and pressure, some rocks near the bottom tend to flow.	(iv) Temperature is 400°C and pressure 3.7 million times the atmospheric pressure.
(v) It provides all the necessary factors for the existence of life.	(v) Density increases as we go down.	
	(vi) The uppermost part of the mantle consists of molten rock called *magma*.	

Fig. 1.4 Layers of the earth

 **Recall**

- The earth consists of three layers—the crust, the mantle and the core.
- The crust is the outermost layer and it provides all the factors necessary for the existence of life.
- The mantle is the layer below the crust.
- The uppermost part of the mantle consists of molten rocks called magma.
- The innermost part of the earth is called the core. It contains metals like iron.

 **Let's Answer**

1. What are the three layers of the earth?
2. In which layer of the earth can coal be found?
3. Which is the region between the crust and the core?
4. What is the core of the earth made up of?
5. Why is the crust layer very important?

EARTH'S ATMOSPHERE

The atmosphere is the blanket of air that surrounds the earth. It extends from the earth's surface to about 965 km above.

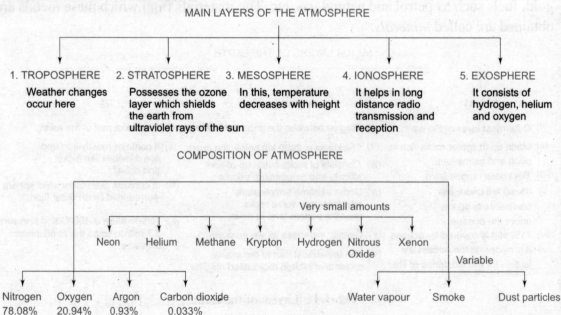

MAIN LAYERS OF THE ATMOSPHERE

1. TROPOSPHERE — Weather changes occur here
2. STRATOSPHERE — Possesses the ozone layer which shields the earth from ultraviolet rays of the sun
3. MESOSPHERE — In this, temperature decreases with height
4. IONOSPHERE — It helps in long distance radio transmission and reception
5. EXOSPHERE — It consists of hydrogen, helium and oxygen

COMPOSITION OF ATMOSPHERE

Very small amounts: Neon, Helium, Methane, Krypton, Hydrogen, Nitrous Oxide, Xenon

Nitrogen 78.08% Oxygen 20.94% Argon 0.93% Carbon dioxide 0.033%

Variable: Water vapour, Smoke, Dust particles

Fig. 1.5   Layers and composition of the atmosphere

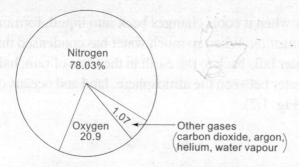

Nitrogen
78.03%

1.07

Oxygen
20.9

Other gases
(carbon dioxide, argon,
helium, water vapour)

Fig. 1.6 (a)   Composition of air

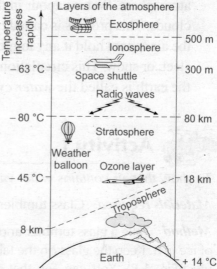

Temperature increases rapidly

Layers of the atmosphere

Exosphere

Ionosphere — 500 m

Space shuttle — 300 m

Radio waves

−63 °C

−80 °C   Stratosphere — 80 km

Weather balloon

Ozone layer

−45 °C — 18 km

Troposphere

8 km

Earth

+ 14 °C

Fig. 1.6 (b)   Layers of the atmosphere

ROLE OF ATMOSPHERE

The atmosphere plays a very important role in the survival of life on earth. It helps in the following ways:

1. It acts like a blanket to protect life on earth. Heat and light from the sun fall on the uppermost layer of the atmosphere which reflects or absorbs most of it. As a result only a part of the heat and light reach the surface of the earth and so the earth's surface is neither too hot nor too cold.

2. Movement of air. The amount of heat and light received at different places on the earth's surface keeps changing throughout the year.

   At a particular place, it may change everyday and also during the day. This allows the movement of air from the hotter to the colder areas resulting in winds, storms, cyclones, etc.

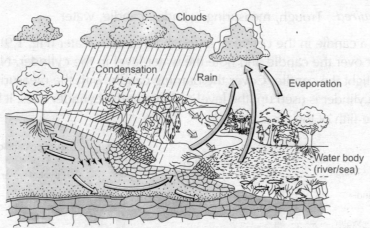

Fig. 1.7   Water cycle

3. Water changes into water vapour upon evaporation. Evaporation of water takes place continuously due to the heat of the sun and the water vapour becomes a part of the

atmosphere. Water vapour in the air when it cools changes back into liquid, forming clouds. This process is called *condensation*. When so much water has condensed that the air cannot hold it any longer, water falls back to the earth in the form of rain, hail, sleet, or snow. This circulation of water between the atmosphere, land and oceans on the earth is called the *water cycle* (Fig. 1.7).

Activity 1

To show that air contains water vapour.

Materials required   Glass tumbler, ice.

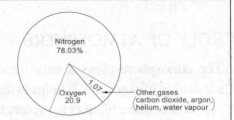

Fig. 1.8   Air contains water vapour

Method   Take a glass tumbler and put a few pieces of ice in it. Keep the glass on the table for a few minutes (Fig. 1.8). You can see that droplets of water appear on the outer surface of the glass. Where do the droplets come from?

As the air around the glass comes in contact with the cold glass, water vapour in the air condenses on the glass to form water.

Activity 2

To show that air contains oxygen.

Materials required   Trough, measuring cylinder, candle, water.

Method   Fix a candle in the centre of a trough filled with water (Fig. 1.9). Place a measuring cylinder over the candle and note the water level in the cylinder. Now remove the cylinder and light the candle. Cover the burning candle with the measuring cylinder. As the air in the cylinder is used up, the level of water in the cylinder rises. It has been found that about one-fifth of the air is used up.

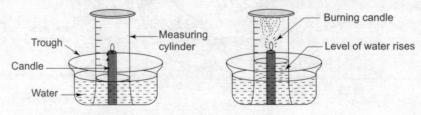

Fig. 1.9   About one-fifth of air is used up in burning

Activity 3

To test for the presence of CO_2 in air.

Materials required Test tube, cork, two delivery tubes (one long and one short), lime-water.

Method Take some freshly pre-pared lime-water in a test tube. Fit a cork and two delivery tubes (one long) and (one short) into the mouth of the test tube as shown in the Figure 1.10.

Suck air through the shorter delivery tube. You will observe some bubbles in the lime-water. This happens because air from outside (containing carbon dioxide) is drawn in through the other delivery tube.

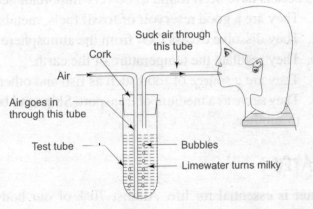

Fig. 1.10 To show that the air contains carbon dioxide

Recall

- The main layers of the atmosphere are the troposphere, stratosphere, mesosphere, iono-sphere and the exosphere.
- The atmosphere acts like a blanket protecting life on earth.
- Air contains water vapour, carbon dioxide and oxygen which are very essential for the survival of life on earth.
- Lime-water turns milky showing the presence of carbon dioxide.

Let's Answer

1. Name the two main gases found in air.
2. By what process do we get salt from seawater?
3. What is the importance of the presence of CO_2 in the atmosphere?
4. What is the proportion of CO_2 in air?

THE OCEANS

More than two-thirds of the earth's surface is covered by seas and oceans. The five oceans on the earth are the Pacific, Atlantic, Indian, Arctic, and the Antarctic Ocean. Their average depth is 3.5 km. The Pacific is the largest and the deepest. The ocean beds have a variety of physical features such as plains, mountains, valleys, etc.

Importance of Oceans

The oceans have been found to be very important because of the following reasons:
1. They are a good reservoir of fossil fuels, metals and salts.
2. They dissolve excess CO_2 from the atmosphere.
3. They regulate the temperature of the earth.
4. They are a source of food such as fish and other edible marine life.
5. They serve as a medium of transport. Ships and boats are used to sail from one country to another.

WATER

Water is essential for life. Almost 70% of our body weight is due to water. It is vital because of the following reasons:
1. It is a very good solvent.
2. Plants absorb minerals dissolved in water from the soil.
3. Water cools and heats at a slower rate compared to land, so the temperature variations in oceans and lakes are not very wide. This helps marine life to thrive.
4. During the day land heats up faster than water, so a cool breeze flows from the sea to the land. At night the land cools faster than the sea, so cool winds blow from the land to the sea. That is why coastal areas have a moderate climate.
5. Ice is lighter than water so it floats helping marine life to survive even in extremely cold conditions. This is because the thick floating layer of ice prevents further cooling of the water below it.
6. Food cannot be absorbed by our body until it is converted into substances that can dissolve in water.

SOIL

It is the topmost layer of the earth's crust. It is another factor favouring the existence of life on earth. It is important because:
1. Plants need soil to obtain minerals and water.
2. It gives shelter to a number of insects, reptiles and other animals.
3. Soil varies from place to place so the type of plants and animals in a particular place also depends on the nature of the soil. For example, camels are found only in deserts.

Recall

- Two-thirds of the earth's surface is covered by oceans.
- Oceans are a reservoir of fossil fuels and food, and help in regulating the temperature of the earth. They also acts as a medium of transport.
- Water is very essential for both plant and animal life as it is a good solvent.
- Soil is the uppermost layer of the earth's crust. It helps the plants and animals to survive by helping them in obtaining nutrition.

 **Let's Answer**

1. Mention two important properties of water that make it a special liquid.
2. "Soil is important for the existence of life on earth". Explain.
3. Name three important materials that are obtained from the ocean.
4. What fraction of the earth is covered by oceans?

THE EARTH AND THE SOLAR SYSTEM

Heavenly bodies revolving, each in a definite elliptical orbit, around the sun are called *planets*. The earth is one of the nine planets in our solar system.

Sun, the nine planets, their moons, and the other heavenly bodies that revolve around the sun form the *solar system* (Fig. 1.11).

 Do You Know?

1. Nicolaus Copernicus (1473–1593), a polish astronomer proposed that the sun is at the centre of the universe and that the earth and other planets revolved around the sun.
2. The equator once ran near the south pole.
3. Cosmonaut Yuri Gagarin made the first orbit of the earth.
4. Aryabhata (AD 476–520), famous mathematician. He was a native of Kerala who lived in Kusumpura (Patna). At the age of 23 he wrote his small but famous work on astronomy, the *Aryabhatiya*. It has 118 verses—a summary of Hindu mathematics of that time.

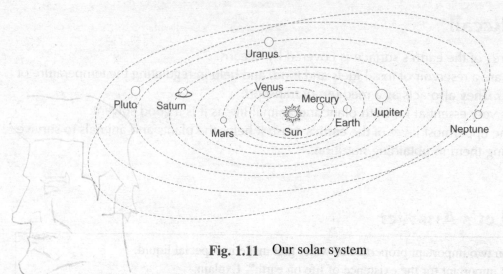

Fig. 1.11 Our solar system

In the solar system the planet closest to the sun is *mercury*. It is smaller than the earth and its gravitational force is not enough to hold on to an atmosphere. Therefore, light and heat from the sun reach the surface directly. So one part which faces the sun is very hot while the other part away from the sun is very cold.

The next planet is *Venus*. It is of the same size as that of the earth. Venus has an atmosphere that mainly consists of carbon dioxide, water vapour and oxygen. It traps a lot of heat and is the hottest planet in the solar system. The atmosphere of Venus reflects back a lot of the sunlight that falls on it. Venus, therefore, appears to be the brightest planet in the sky.

The Earth is the third planet from the sun. It has an atmosphere with gases which support life. Being at the right distance from the sun it is neither too hot nor too cold. The earth's atmosphere helps to maintain the right temperature.

The next planet is *Mars*. It is a red, rocky planet about half the size of the earth. The atmosphere is thinner than that of the earth. The surface is covered with craters (depressions) and hillocks (mountains). It is a cold planet with temperatures remaining below the freezing point.

In 1996 scientists discovered fossils of some early forms of life on Mars.

The polar regions of Mars were found to be covered with a white material which disappeared after a few months. So scientists thought about the possible presence of ice. However, rocks and soil have not given any evidence for the presence of water or of life on the planet.

Jupiter is next and is the largest known planet with a large red spot on its surface. The spot is due to a giant storm that has been going on for years. It is a cold planet as it is far away from the sun.

Saturn is the second largest planet with several wide rings. These rings are made up of dust and ice. It is also a very cold planet.

Uranus, Neptune and *Pluto* are farther away from the sun and hence are very cold. Pluto is the smallest planet.

Other heavenly bodies that are a part of the solar system are moons or satellites of the planets, asteroids, meteors, and comets.

Recall

- Heavenly bodies revolving, each in a definite elliptical orbit, around the sun are called planets.
- Sun, the nine planets, their moons and other heavenly bodies that revolve around the sun form the solar system.

Let's Answer

1. Name the two planets between the (a) sun and the earth and (b) between which earth is located.
2. Why is there no life on the planet Mercury?
3. How many planets are there in the solar system?
4. Why is Venus the brightest of all the planets visible?
5. Which planet has a red spot?

Do You Know?

Are we alone?

Astronomers use telescopes to study heavenly bodies. Scientists have also sent spaceships into space and even to other planets like Mars. In April 1990, scientists were able to launch the Hubble Telescope which gives a better view of the heavenly bodies. There are space observatories, fitted with powerful telescopes, that are continuously collecting information about heavenly bodies and sending them back to the earth. But scientists have not been able to find any definite evidence that may indicate the existence of life beyond the earth.

 **Recall**

- The oceans play a very important role in many natural processes.
- Water has many special properties that are necessary for the existence of life.
- The soil provides minerals and water to plants and helps them grow.
- The solar system consists of the sun and the nine planets revolving around it.
- The earth fulfils all the conditions necessary for the existence of life.
- So far scientists have not found any evidence of life beyond the earth.

EXERCISES

1. **Choose the appropriate answer**

    (i) The hottest part of the earth is the

    (a) mantle   (b) troposphere

    (c) core   (d) stratosphere

    (ii) Which of the following gases protect us from ultraviolet rays?

    (a) Helium   (b) Ozone

    (c) Carbon dioxide   (d) Argon

    (iii) Which planet does not have an atmosphere?

    (a) Venus   (b) Saturn

    (c) Jupiter   (d) Pluto

    (iv) Which layer of the atmosphere do we live in?

    (a) Mesosphere   (b) Ionosphere

    (c) Troposphere   (d) Stratosphere

    (v) The sun is at the centre of the

    (a) galaxy   (b) universe

    (c) solar system   (d) none of the above

    (vi) The earth completes one revolution in

    (a) 24 hours   (b) 365 days

    (c) $364\frac{1}{5}$ days   (c) $365\frac{1}{4}$ days

    (vii) The planet farthest from the sun is

    (a) the earth   (b) Jupiter

    (c) Pluto   (d) Saturn

    (viii) Which of the following is/are necessary for life?

    (a) Right temperature   (b) Presence of water

    (c) Presence of oxygen   (d) All of the above

    (ix) Which of the following is the natural satellite of the earth?

    (a) Jupiter   (b) Moon

    (c) Mars   (d) Pluto

2. **Mark the following sentences as *True* or *False***

   (a) The earth is a unique planet.

   (b) Mars is a black-coloured planet.

   (c) Venus has a high level of CO_2 in its atmosphere.

   (d) The central region between the crust and the core of the earth is called the mantle.

   (e) Pluto is the planet nearest to the sun.

3. **Fill in the blanks**

   (a) The planet Mercury has no _____.

   (b) The temperature on the earth's surface is controlled by _____.

   (c) The gas present in maximum proportion in air is _____.

   (d) The mesosphere comes after the _____.

   (e) Mercury is called the _____ planet.

4. **Match the columns**

A	B
(a) Satellite	(i) Pacific
(b) Ocean	(ii) Carbon dioxide
(c) Crust	(iii) Moon
(d) Venus	(iv) Rotation
(e) Day and night	(v) Iron

5. **Give one word for the following**

   (a) Name the
      (i) planet with rings
      (ii) smallest planet
      (iii) hottest planet
      (iv) planet with the largest number of moons

   (b) In which layer of the earth is magma found?

   (c) Name the five oceans.

   (d) Which movement of the earth is responsible for day and night?

   (e) Which gas present in the atmosphere is essential for the survival of life?

   (f) The ozone layer protects us from which rays of the sun?

   (g) Who made the first orbit of the earth?

   (h) Name the two planets whose orbits cross each other.

6. **Answer the following questions briefly**

   (a) Why does your bathroom mirror get misty after you have had a hot water bath in winters?

   (b) What do you mean by the term *ocean*?

   (c) Mention two properties of water that make it a special liquid.

   (d) What is the cause of change of seasons?

(e) What is the difference between a planet and a star?

(f) What is magma?

(g) What do you understand by the term *axis*?

7. **Answer the following questions in detail**

(a) Describe the factors essential for the survival of life on earth?

(b) With the help of a diagram explain the internal structure of the earth.

(c) Why is soil an essential requirement for the existence of life on earth?

(d) With the help of an experiment prove the presence of carbon dioxide in the atmosphere.

(e) Explain the importance of the atmosphere.

(f) Discuss the importance of oceans for us.

(g) Ice is lighter than water. How does this contribute to the survival of marine life?

(h) Mercury is the closest planet to the sun yet Venus is hotter than Mercury. Justify.

THINK AND ANSWER

1. How was the first rocket fuelled?

2. Why does the sun look the same size as the moon?

3. Why is it not safe to look at the sun through smoked glass?

4. What is often called the sun's atmosphere?

 Teacher's Notes

- **My Very Educated Mother Just Showed Us Nine Planets**
  The first letter of each word in the sentence gives the name of the planet, and the exact order.
  M — Mercury; V — Venus; E — Earth; M — Mars; J — Jupiter; S — Saturn; U — Uranus; N — Neptune; P — Pluto.

- The teacher can instruct the student to observe the night sky and to try and recognize the constellations, bright stars and planets which are visible.

- A visit to the planetarium would certainly make the chapter more interesting.

2

- Environment
- Biotic environment—producers, consumers, decomposers
- Interactions in the environment
- Abiotic environment—air, water, soil, light, temperature
- Socio-cultural environment

Our Environment

Take a look around you—this amazing variety of plants, animals, insects, air, water, soil, etc., all form a part of your surroundings. If you happen to travel from the hills to the plains or to the coastal areas, you can feel the change in climate. You will also find that plants, animals, food, even the clothing of the people are different. It very much depends on the climatic factors, which are different in different parts of the world.

ENVIRONMENT

The physical and biological world in which we live is called our *environment*.

There is a continuous interaction between living organisms and the non-living part of the environment. Plants, animals, and human beings, including micro-organisms, constitute the *biotic component* of the environment. Air, water, light, temperature, and soil constitute the *abiotic component*.

Human beings form an important part of this environment. Gifted with a powerful brain, humans have been able to change or modify the natural environment to suit their requirements. This is called forming the *socio-cultural environment* (Fig. 2.1).

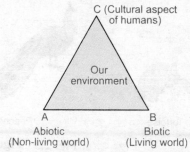

Fig. 2.1   The three components of our environment

BIOTIC ENVIRONMENT

The biotic component of the environment includes all living organisms in a given area. Living things can vary in shape, size, habit, habitat, and even structure.

Living organisms are of the following three types depending on their food habits (Fig. 2.2):

 (a) Producers or autotrophs
 (b) Consumers or heterotrophs
 (c) Decomposers

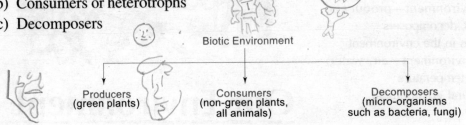

Biotic Environment

Producers
(green plants)

Consumers
(non-green plants,
all animals)

Decomposers
(micro-organisms
such as bacteria, fungi)

Fig. 2.2   Biotic environment

Some of these living organisms are so small that they are not visible to us with the naked eye. We need a lens or a microscope to study these organisms. They are called *micro-organisms*. We will now learn about the role of various living organisms in the biotic environment.

Activity 1

 (i) Collect samples of local plants of the place you visited.
 (ii) Find out their local and scientific names.
 (iii) Place the samples between the pages of a newspaper and put a heavy weight on top.
 (iv) After the sample leaves have dried up make a scrap book. Combine them to form different patterns as shown in Figure 2.3.

Tortoise   Peacock   Elephant

Fig. 2.3   Figures made of dried leaves

Producers or Autotrophs

Green plants which can prepare their own food with the help of *chlorophyll* in the presence of *sunlight*, *carbon dioxide* from *air*, and *water* and *minerals* from the soil are called *producers*. And this process is known as *photosynthesis*.

Green plants help animals by making food, releasing oxygen and using up the carbon dioxide given out by animals during respiration (Fig. 2.4).

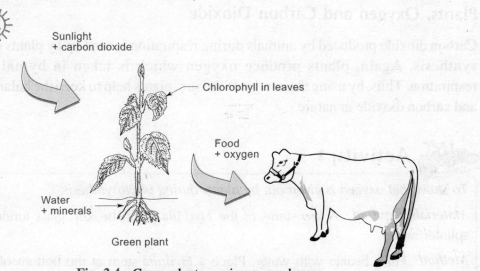

Fig. 2.4   Green plants—primary producers

All plants are not green. Such non-green plants lack chlorophyll and cannot prepare their own food and so depend on green plants for their nutrition.

Activity 2

To grow non-green plants.

Materials required   Piece of bread, a bottle, water.

Method   Place a piece of bread in the bottle. Add a little water so that the bread is quite wet. Leave the bottle in a cupboard for a few days, and then observe the change. What do you see?

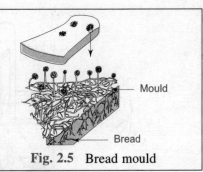

Fig. 2.5   Bread mould

A soft substance like fur will appear after some time on the bread. This is called *mould* (Fig. 2.5) which belongs to the fungus group.

Dependence of Animals on Plants

Animals are dependent on plants for the following reasons:
  (a) **Food**   Animals depend on plants directly or indirectly for food.
  (b) **Oxygen**   Plants give out oxygen during photosynthesis.
  (c) **Shelter**   Birds, arboreal animals, ants, snakes, insects, etc., depend on plants for shelter.

Plants, Oxygen and Carbon Dioxide

Carbon dioxide produced by animals during respiration is used up by plants during photosynthesis. Again, plants produce oxygen which is taken in by animals during respiration. Thus, by using the energy of the sun, plants help to keep the balance of oxygen and carbon dioxide in nature.

 ## Activity 3

To show that oxygen is given out by plants during photosynthesis.

Materials required   A few stems of the *Hydrilla* plant, beaker, glass funnel, test tube, splinter, water.

Method   Fill a beaker with water. Place a *Hydrilla* stem at the bottom of the beaker. Invert a glass funnel with a short stem over the *Hydrilla* plant. Invert a test tube filled with water over the funnel stalk. Leave the whole setup in bright sunlight. After about a week, lift the test tube but do not let any air enter the test tube. Put your thumb over the mouth of the tube and lift it out of the beaker. Test for the presence of oxygen by introducing a glowing splinter in the tube (Fig. 2.6).

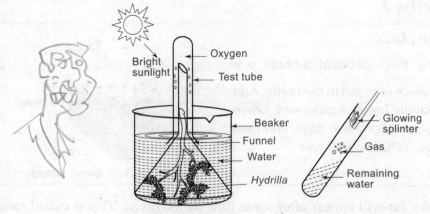

Fig. 2.6   Oxygen is given out during photosynthesis

In the above activity the glowing splinter will burn brighter confirming that the gas in the tube is oxygen.

You will now understand why it is necessary to add water plants to an aquarium. Do you think the water plants can be substituted with an air pump?

Dependence of Plants on Animals

Plants depend on animals for the following:

1. Plants need animals for pollination (Fig. 2.7).

Fig. 2.7   Insects help in pollination

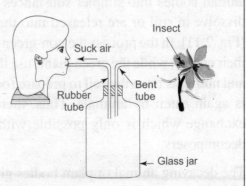

Fig. 2.8   Animals help in seed dispersal

2. Seeds are dispersed by animals and humans unknowingly (Fig. 2.8). Often, after eating a fruit we throw away the seeds which get carried away to distant places.

3. The excreta of animals, and the decomposed bodies of animals and dead plants add nutrients to the soil. This manure is a source of minerals for the green plants.

Activity 4

To collect small insects.

Materials required   Straws, glass jar.

Method   Make tubes from bent straws or from ball point pens which can be bent by heating them. Set up the apparatus as shown in Figure 2.9. Place one tube near an insect and suck air through the other. The insect is drawn into the bottle. Repeat the process to collect more specimens.

Fig. 2.9   To collect small insects in a jar

Consumers or Heterotrophs

They depend directly or indirectly on producers for their food. All animals are called *consumers* because they cannot make their own food. They are also called *heterotrophs*. Consumers are of the following three types (Fig. 2.10):

Some animals help us by consuming the dead bodies of other animals. These animals, such as, jackals, crows, and vultures are called *scavengers*. They help to clean up the environment.

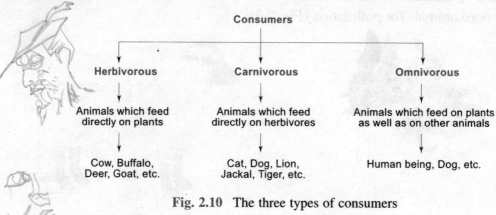

Fig. 2.10   The three types of consumers

Decomposers

Every living organism has a definite lifespan after which it dies. These dead bodies of plants and animals are broken down into simpler substances by some micro-organisms (non-green plants) which are known as *decomposers*. The process is called *decomposition*.

For example, fungi such as toadstools and mushrooms break down the compounds present in dead plant and animal bodies into simpler substances which either dissolve in soil or are released into the atmosphere (Fig. 2.11). In the process the non-green plants obtain their energy, while the green plants use these minerals and nutrients from the soil to prepare food. This food is again eaten by animals. Thus, there is a cyclic exchange which is only possible with the help of decomposers.

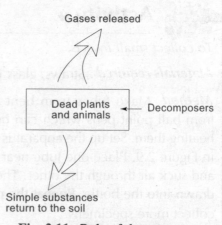

Fig. 2.11   Role of decomposers

The decaying animal or plant bodies give off an unpleasant smell. We can thus realize when food is going bad by the foul-smelling gases that are released. Without decomposers, dead plants and animals would pile up. Just imagine how many dead things there would be now, in a world without decomposers! However, all objects cannot be decomposed.

Do You Know?

- The largest mammal without a backbone is the giant squid.
- The unusual thing about a snake's tongue is that it is forked.
- The creature which is said to commit mass 'suicide' when migrating is the Lemming.

Recall

- The physical and biological world in which we live is called our environment.
- Plants and animals form the biotic component of the environment.
- Soil, water, air, light, and temperature form the abiotic component of the environment.
- Plants depend on animals and animals also depend on plants for various reasons.
- Micro-organisms are decomposers.

Let's Answer

1. What is environment?
2. How do plants depend on animals?
3. How do animals depend on plants?
4. Explain how micro-organisms help us.
5. Consumers can be categorized into three different kinds. Explain with the help of examples.

INTERACTIONS IN THE ENVIRONMENT

We have seen that plants depend on animals and also that animals use the food prepared by plants. Again, we have the decomposers who are responsible for recycling minerals. Thus, we find that there is a constant interaction among the living and non-living components of the environment.

Ecosystem and Balance in Nature

Any area or place where living organisms and non-living things co-exist, exchanging the materials necessary for life and using them again and again is called an ecosystem. It may be a forest, garden, field, river, pond, or even a lake.

An ecosystem consists of four parts—the *non-living* part, the *green plants* (producers), the *consumers* and the *decomposers*.

The space occupied by a biotic community is called its *habitat*. A habitat includes both biotic and abiotic components.

Nature tries to maintain a balance so that all organisms can live happily in the ecosystem without harming the existence of others. This balance maintained in nature is known as the *ecological balance*.

Let us study the balance of nature in a field. In a field, plants are grown by a farmer. These are eaten by insects. The insects, in turn, are eaten by birds. Plants require water, air and soil to survive. If there is a shortage of any of these, plants will die. If plants die, so will the insects. If insects die, the birds in that area would also die due to starvation.

Now, let us look at it backwards. If all the birds die, then insects would increase in number. They would feed on all the plants and destroy the whole crop. If the crops are destroyed, we will not get sufficient food and would be affected. This shows that if we disturb any part of the ecosystem, we disturb the balance in nature.

In the biosphere there is a natural control of one organism over another. If there is an increase in the number of insects, birds would have more to eat and thereby they would increase in number. If there is a decrease in the number of insects, there would be a corresponding decrease in the number of birds too.

Thus we see that all living forms not only depend on one another, but also control or keep a check on each other. This process helps in maintaining the balance in nature.

 ## Do You Know?

- The sea-horse is a fish.
- The hippopotamus is known as the *River Horse*.
- The jellyfish is known as the *Portuguese-Man-of-War*.
- The pig is the only non-human creature to suffer sunburns.

Food Chain

In nature you would have observed a large number of organisms. They are all dependent on one another. One organism eats another organism and in turn is eaten by another animal. Thus, there is a link between the various organisms based on their food requirements.

Plants produce their own food using the non-living components of nature like air, soil and sunlight. Herbivorous animals eat these plants. Carnivorous animals eat herbivorous animals and other smaller carnivores, and so on. The whole cycle of who-eats-whom forms the *food chain*. *A food chain shows the feeding relationship between different organisms in a natural environment*. It always begins with a green plant, the producer (Fig. 2.12).

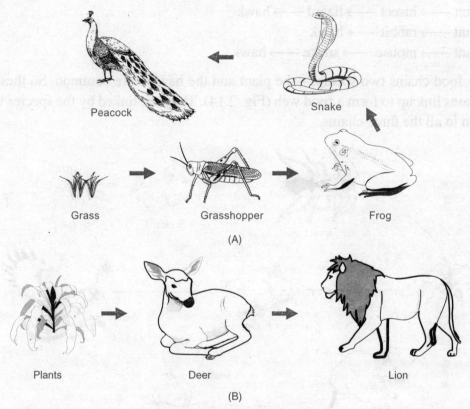

(A)

(B)

Fig. 2.12   Two food chains

Activity 5

Materials required   Stiff cardboard, scissors.

Method   Cut links from the stiff cardboard in the form of rings.

Fig. 2.13   Model of a food chain

23

Food Webs

There are a number of food chains in the biosphere. Many such food chains are linked to each other to form a *food web*. These different food chains which make up a food web usually have one or more species in common. These species form the link between two food chains. For example, consider the following food chains:

1. Plant ⟶ insect ⟶ lizard ⟶ hawk
2. Plant ⟶ rabbit ⟶ hawk
3. Plant ⟶ mouse ⟶ snake ⟶ hawk

In these food chains two species—the plant and the hawk—are common. So these three food chains link up to form a food web (Fig. 2.14). They are linked by the species that are common to all the three chains.

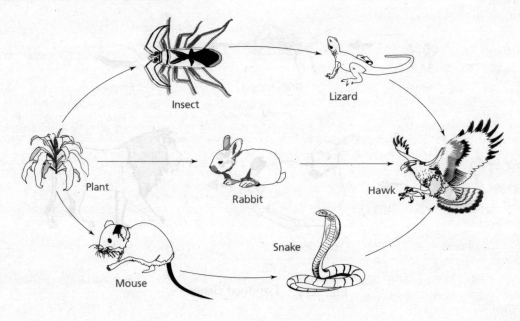

Fig. 2.14   Food web formed by three food chains

 # Activity 6

Materials required   Cardboard, old magazines.

Method   Take a few cards and stick pictures of plants, insects and animals taken from old magazines.

(Contd...)

Then arrange them to show the link and form a food chain and then a food web.

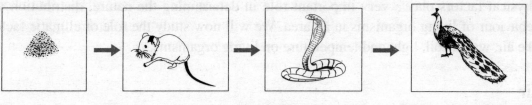

Fig. 2.15

 Activity 7

When you visit any place during your holidays or otherwise, do not disturb the plants and animals in that area. Now make a record of your observations.

Introduction What is your aim	Method What did you see or did? where and how?	Results and observation	Conclusion

Fig. 2.16

 Recall

- All living forms not only depend on one another but control or keep a check on each other.
- Energy flows from plants to animals through food chains.
- Food chains are inter-linked to form a food web.
- An area where living organisms and non-living things co-exist, exchanging materials necessary for life and using them again and again forms an ecosystem.

 Let's Answer

1. Observe various plants and animals around you. List them down and draw the food chains of as many as you can.
2. What is a food web?
3. Explain the term *ecological balance*.
4. Why do we say energy flows from plants to animals?

ABIOTIC OR PHYSICAL ENVIRONMENT

Physical factors play a very important role in determining the nature, distribution and behaviour of living organisms in an area. We will now study the role of climatic factors like air, water, soil, light and temperature on living organisms.

Air

Air is a mixture of gases like oxygen, carbon dioxide, nitrogen, and argon. The presence of oxygen in air influences all living organisms because they use it for respiration. The amounts of these gases varies from place to place. The cycling of oxygen and carbon dioxide between the living and non-living components in the environment is essential to keep the balance in nature.

Air also contains water vapour and dust particles which protect us from the strong ultra-violet rays of the sun.

Air currents are called *wind*. Strong winds can uproot huge trees. Forest fires can also be spread by wind. Wind helps in (i) dispersal of seeds, (ii) pollination, and (iii) dispersal of pollutants.

Water

Life is not possible without water. It is one of the most important requirements of living organisms. Plants and animals adapt themselves according to the amount of water available in the surroundings.

The distribution of water on the surface of the earth varies from place to place.

Water can dissolve gases like oxygen and carbon dioxide. Heating and cooling of water is slow as compared to air. Water below the ice in frozen lakes and oceans remains in the liquid form. This enables aquatic animals to survive even during severe winters.

Water is necessary for

  (i) irrigation
(iii) growth of plants
  (v) digestion and excretion

(ii) germination of seeds
(iv) absorption of nutrients

There are many sources of water. Rain and snow are the primary sources.

Soil

It is another important component of the physical environment. It varies in structure and chemical composition.

Soil is essential for the growth of plants. Different types of plants require different types of soil for their growth. Soil contains water in the form of moisture. It also contains air. Soil provides minerals to the plant.

Different areas allow the growth of different types of vegetables and crops depending on the nutrient and water content of the soil. Sometimes, manure and fertilizers are added to enrich the soil.

Light

Light is important for all living organisms. It helps us to see things around us and sunlight is vital in the process of photosynthesis.

The intensity and the amount of sunlight differs in different parts of the world.

In thick forests the big trees block a lot of the sun's rays from falling on the earth. So only small plants and animals can grow on the ground (Fig. 2.17).

Light also penetrates water bodies but it depends on and varies with the depth.

Fig. 2.17   Dense forest—light penetration is very less

Some animals get affected by light. Insects, moles and earthworms tend to remain underground during daytime.

Temperature

It is a measure of the degree of hotness or coldness of a body. Temperature is measured with the help of a device called the *thermometer*. There is great variation in temperatures on the surface of the earth. The range of temperature at a place during a year controls the distribution and presence of living organisms in that place. A polar bear will not be able to survive in the hot, dry desert. Similarly, cactus cannot grow in extremely cold areas (Fig. 2.18).

Every organism has a temperature tolerance range. The temperature at which a living organism is most comfortable is termed its *optimum temperature*.

Some animals become inactive and escape the extremes of temperature by hiding themselves in holes or burrows. This is called *hibernation*. Some plants reduce their activities, such as transpiration and photosynthesis, in winters.

 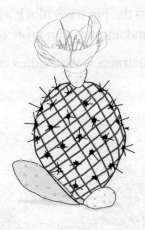

Fig. 2.18   (a) Polar bear (b) Cactus

 Recall

- The abiotic components are very important for all living beings.
- However, the abiotic factors are not the same at all places on the earth.
- Organisms that can adapt themselves to the type of abiotic factors present in their area can survive in that area.

Let's Answer

1. What are the abiotic factors of the environment?
2. Why do plants need (a) soil and (b) light for their growth?
3. How can altitude affect animals?
4. What do you understand by the term *optimum temperature*?

SOCIO-CULTURAL ENVIRONMENT

The influence of human activities on the other components—both living and non-living—of the environment forms the *socio-cultural aspect of the environment*.

In large towns and cities, millions of people live in a small area. What happens when many animals live together in limited space like in a zoo or a cage? If the zoo keeper does not clean out the wastes in the cages, bacteria would infect the animals.

What happens to all the wastes generated by people in a large city or town? What would happen if the sewage was pumped into the sea? Wastes or sewage contain a lot of nutrients which green plants need for growth. When sewage flows into rivers or the sea, the number of decomposers and green plants like algae increase because of the added nutrients. What happens then to the other organisms in the water?

The decomposers grow very fast and use up all the oxygen in the water. As a result, fish and other aquatic animals die due to lack of oxygen. This is how we have dead lakes. Hussain Sagar lake in Hyderabad is an example of a dead lake.

POLLUTION BY HUMAN BEINGS

Every house produces a huge amount of waste in the form of garbage, bath water, kitchen waste, and sewage. Are we upsetting the balance of life in the environment around us by carelessly pouring out wastes? Just imagine what would happen to us and our way of life if we upset the balance of animal and plant life on land and in water? This is something we must all think about.

We litter our surroundings indiscriminately. Decomposers take a lot of time to act. In cities, we throw away aluminium cans, glass bottles and polythene bags. These cannot be naturally decomposed into harmless things.

Materials which can be easily decomposed are known as *biodegradable matter.* Examples are paper and cloth. These materials can be recycled.

But there are also substances which cannot be decomposed naturally. They are called *non-biodegradable* substances. Plastic is one such example. Plastic bags can block drains, choke the sewage and burning them can produce poisonous gases that pollute the air. Sometimes, along with discarded waste, plastics bags are eaten up by cattle, which is very harmful for them.

So, we must take care of our environment by using plastic bags and metal cans less often, and throw them in dust bins after use so that the town municipality can properly recycle them using recycling machines.

Motor vehicles are mainly responsible for increasing the amount of carbon dioxide in the air. City roads especially are full of cars, buses, trucks, etc. These not only produce carbon dioxide but also carbon monoxide and other gases, which are very harmful to us.

From cars, chimneys or anything burning comes out a cloudy mass of suspended particles called *smoke.* Blowing wind disperses the smoke and it spreads far and wide in the atmosphere.

Smoke can get mixed with water vapour and suspended particles in air to form what is called *smog.*

Excessive use of pesticides like DDT is another menace. These, too, cannot be decomposed into harmless substances. So they easily pass into a food chain and a food web, weakening or killing animals all the way.

With lesser trees, there is a lower uptake of carbon dioxide from the atmosphere by plants, less release of oxygen into the atmosphere and a greater occurrence of soil erosion. Urbanization has also led to the setting up of a number of industries which pollute the air, water and land.

The increase in human population is the prime cause for disturbance of the balance in nature. To meet the demands of a growing population, we have set up many industries and cut down trees to build houses. As a result, many animals have now become *extinct*, while some are on the verge of *extinction.*

All of us need air to breathe, water to drink, and a place to live and grow plants. However, the air is contaminated by smoke, water with sewage, and the soil with pesticides, etc. Pesticides, smoke and sewage are *pollutants. The process of making air, water and soil harmful by these pollutants is called pollution.*

You must have realized by now that we depend entirely on natural resources for a comfortable and happy existence. At your age, you can observe and find out measures of avoiding degradation of the environment. Most people love plants and animals, and we should all try to make society aware of the need to conserve nature.

 Recall

- An environment has two main components—abiotic and biotic.
- The abiotic components are air, water, soil, light, and temperature.
- The biotic components are the living organisms, i.e., producers, consumers and decomposers.
- The whole cycle of interaction between the biotic and the abiotic environment forms the ecosystem.
- In nature there is a balance in the ecosystem which is delicately maintained.

EXERCISES

1. **Choose the appropriate answer**
   (i) Which is an omnivore?
      (a) Lion
      (b) Dog
      (c) Sheep
      (d) Cow
   (ii) Decomposers include
      (a) human beings
      (b) bacteria
      (c) fungi
      (d) (b) and (c)
   (iii) Which is a carnivore?
      (a) Tiger
      (b) Rabbit
      (c) Cow
      (d) All of the above
   (iv) Scavengers eat
      (a) plants
      (b) fruits
      (c) vegetables
      (d) dead flesh
   (v) The ultimate source of energy for all living organisms is/are
      (a) human beings
      (b) the sun
      (c) plants
      (d) science and technology

2. **Mark the sentences as *True* or *False***
   (a) Producers are heterotrophs.
   (b) The ultimate source of energy for all organisms are green plants.
   (c) Meat-eating animals are called herbivores.
   (d) The survival of all living things is dependent on each other.
   (e) Humans, being supreme, do not depend on other organisms.

31

(f) Green plants take in both carbon dioxide and oxygen.

(g) Wool is obtained from the fur of sheep.

(h) Paper is made from wood pulp.

(i) Plants convert solar energy into the chemical energy of food.

(j) The socio-cultural environment does not influence the character of human beings.

3. Fill in the blanks

(a) The two major components of the ecosystem are _____ and _____.

(b) Animals that feed on dead fish are called _____.

(c) Interlinked food chains constitute a _____.

(d) Bacteria and fungi act as _____ in the ecosystem.

(e) The primary source of energy for all living organisms is the _____.

(f) The biotic environment means _____.

(g) _____ are decomposers.

(h) _____ is a gas given out by animals but used by plants.

(i) The process of eating and being eaten is termed as forming a _____.

4. Put the food chains in order

(a) Frog → Fly → Sugar → Snake

(b) Lion → Grass → Deer

(c) Seaweed → Shark → Small fish → Big fish

(d) Snake → Plant → Frog → Insect → Peacock

5. Name the following

(a) Three omnivorous animals.

_____   _____   _____

(b) Three animals that live on trees.

_____   _____   _____

(c) Three scavengers.

_____   _____   _____

(d) Three factors essential for the growth of plants.

_____   _____   _____

(e) Three products from plants used by us.

_____   _____   _____

6. Define the following terms

(a) Environment   (b) Ecosystem   (c) Food chain   (d) Food web

(e) Pollution   (f) Hibernation

7. Distinguish between

(a) Herbivores and carnivores   (b) Producers and consumers

(c) Decomposers and scavengers   (d) Habitat and environment

8. **Answer the following questions briefly**
   (a) Why are plants called producers?
   (b) What is meant by the balance in nature?
   (c) How are micro-organisms useful?
   (d) Name three abiotic components of the environment.
   (e) What are heterotrophs? Give two examples.
   (f) Why are you not supposed to sleep under a tree at night?

9. **Justify the following statements**
   (a) No living organism can live by itself.
   (b) We directly or indirectly depend on green plants.

10. **Answer the following questions in detail**
   (a) Explain how decomposers keep the soil fertile.
   (b) In what ways have we upset the balance in nature?
   (c) What would happen if any one of the links is missing in a food chain?
   (d) Why do birds get sick when farmers spray crops with pesticides?
   (e) How does the cutting of trees in a forest affect the environment?
   (f) Why does a person feel uncomfortable while climbing to higher altitudes?
   (g) How does temperature fluctuation affect the environment?
   (h) "Water is essential for every living organism". Discuss the statement.
   (i) How does light and soil help a plant?
   (j) Mention five different ways in which plants are useful to us.
   (k) Is the socio-cultural environment responsible for environmental changes?

THINK AND ANSWER

1. Why aren't plastics good for the environment?
2. Why should we try to protect and save nature's gifts?
3. Disposal of waste should be done in the right manner. Why?
4. We should plant as many trees as possible (not the harmful ones). Why? Which trees do you think can be harmful?

 Teacher's Notes

- A visit to a zoo could be organised to enable students to understand the variety of environments which are created for different living organisms.
- Students could be advised to collect samples of leaves, soil, stones, or feathers of birds from any place they visit as part of a project.

3

- Classification
- Basis of classification
- Matter
- States of matter
- Physical properties of matter

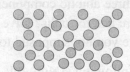

Nature of Matter

In our daily life we come across a wide variety of things. Some of these things are living and some are non-living. Non-living things can either be natural or man-made. In order to understand their features, it is important to classify them.

CLASSIFICATION

While sitting in a classroom you observe many things around you such as desks, chairs, blackboard, doors, fans, bags, water bottles, books, etc. All these objects are not alike and vary from one another in some respect or the other.

 Activity 1

Visit your kitchen and observe the arrangement of utensils there.

You will observe that your mother has put different kinds of utensils in different groups. For example, all the spoons are in one group and all the forks in another. The plates are separately arranged and all the glasses are together, and so on. If such a pattern is not followed, it will be difficult for your mother, or you to find what you are looking for.

We group things for our convenience. In a general store we can shop for various items under one roof. It has separate shelves for soaps, pulses, toothpastes, flour, spices, etc. If these commodities are not grouped separately, the shopkeeper would find it very difficult to locate an item in his shop.

Visit a fruit shop, a chemist store or a library to understand the need for grouping or sorting out things into separate classes. This is known as classification. Thus,

Classification is the process of sorting out and placing things of the same kind together in a separate group or class.

BASIS OF CLASSIFICATION

 ## Activity 2

To find the basis of classification.

Try to classify the balls shown in Figure 3.1(a) in any manner you like.

Next, try to classify the balls shown in Figure 3.1(b) as you wish.

You would find it difficult to form different groups in Figure 3.1(a) as they are alike in all respects. However, in case of Figure 3.1(b), you can easily classify the balls since they have some similarities and some dissimilarities.

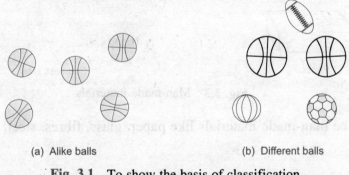

(a) Alike balls   (b) Different balls

Fig. 3.1 To show the basis of classification

From the above activity it is clear that *the basis of classification is the similarity or dissimilarity of objects.*

Let us discuss some of the factors on the basis of which objects may be classified.

On the Basis of Origin of Material

There are two types of objects on the basis of origin of material: *natural* and *man-made*.

Natural and man-made materials   The different things that we see around us are made of different kinds of materials. These materials may be *naturally occurring* such as rock, wood, water, coal, gold, silver, etc. (Fig. 3.2).

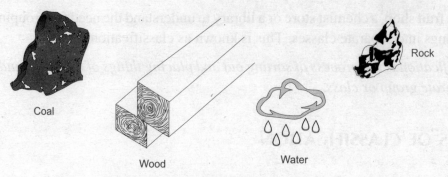

Coal

Wood

Water

Rock

Fig. 3.2   Naturally occurring materials

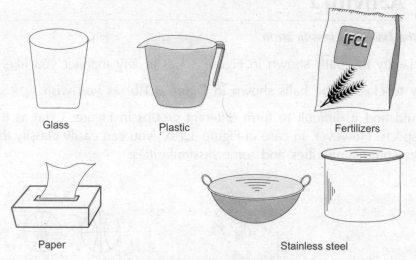

Glass

Plastic

IFCL

Fertilizers

Paper

Stainless steel

Fig. 3.3   Man-made materials

They can also be man-made materials like paper, glass, fibres, steel, bronze, fertilizers, etc. (Fig. 3.3).

On the Basis of Material Used

Often an object can be made from many kinds of materials. For example, a plate can be made from paper, plastic, glass, stainless steel, or silver. A bottle can be made from plastic, glass or even steel. A chair may be made of wood, plastic, iron, or cement. So objects can be classified on the basis of the material used to make them.

Similarly, objects can also be classified on the basis of various other features like:
 (i) weight
 (ii) response to a magnet
(iii) physical state
(iv) colour, etc.

36

Recall

- The objects around us are classified on the basis of their similarities and dissimilarities.
- Things can be grouped on the basis of their shape, size, colour, hardness, etc. They may be classified as living or non-living and in addition to this, may be sorted out as natural or man-made.

MATTER

All objects that we see around us are made up of some kind of material. All these materials or substances are composed of matter. Anything that one can touch, feel, smell, see, or taste is matter. For example, the water that we drink to quench our thirst is matter. The air we breathe in and the ice cream that almost everyone enjoys are also examples of matter.

 Activity 3

To show that a solid has mass.

Materials required   A ball, a stone, a book, an eraser, a balance.

Method   Pick up the ball, the book, the stone, the pencil and the eraser, one at a time. Feel the weight in each case. Some are heavy and some are light.

Now place each item, one at a time, on one pan of the balance. What do you observe? The pan with the object goes down. What does it show?

Fig. 3.4   A solid has mass

 Activity 4

To show that a liquid has mass.

Materials required   Two glasses, water, a balance.

Method   Place an empty glass on one pan of the balance and a similar glass filled with water on the other pan. What do you see? The pan with the glass full of water goes down. This shows that it is heavier. What does this tell us about the water in the glass?

Fig. 3.5   A liquid has mass

Activity 5

To show that a gas has mass.

Materials required   Four identical balloons, balance.

Method   Place two balloons on one pan of the balance.
Now inflate the remaining two balloons and put them on
the other pan of the balance. Which pan is heavier? What
does it show?

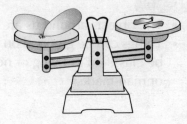

Fig. 3.6   Air has mass

The above experiments show that all solids, liquids and gases, be they big or small, have
mass. Thus,

Matter is anything that has mass.

Activity 6

To show that matter occupies space.

Materials required   Your school bag, a stone, a string, a mug, water, two balloons.

Method   Keep your bag on the table. Can you keep anything exactly in the same place
without removing the bag?

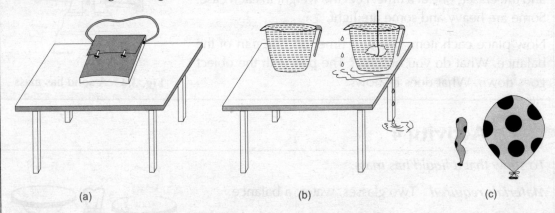

| (a) | (b) | (c) |

Fig. 3.7   Matter occupies space

Now take the empty mug and place it on the table. Pour some water into the mug. Where
has the water gone? It has occupied some space inside the mug [Fig. 3.7 (b)].

(Contd.)

Now tie a string around a stone and try to put the stone into the mug. What will happen? The water in the mug overflows. Why does this happen?

Now take two balloons. Fill one with air and keep the other as it is. Which balloon is bigger? How did it grow in size?

In (a) the answer is no. This shows that the bag has occupied some space on the table.

In (b) the water in the mug overflows because the stone on entering the mug pushes out some of the water and occupies its place [Fig. 3.7 (b)].

In (c) the inflated balloon is obviously bigger and it is the air that you blew in that made it bigger. The air has occupied some space in the balloon [Fig. 3.7 (c)].

Thus, in the above activities we see that the bag, the stone, the water, and the air, all occupy space.

Thus, *matter is anything that has mass and occupies space.*

STATES OF MATTER

Matter can exist in any of the three physical states, i.e., solid, liquid or gas. For example, water (liquid) can exist as ice (solid) as well as water vapour (gas). The change of state depends upon the pressure and temperature conditions. Similarly, carbon dioxide can also occur as solid, liquid or gas.

All the three states of matter are made up of minute particles called *molecules*. The arrangement of molecules is responsible for the existence of the solid, liquid and gaseous states. Figure 3.8 represents the arrangement of molecules in solids, liquids and gases.

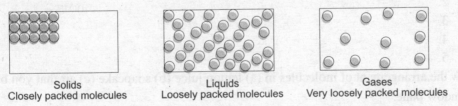

Solids	Liquids	Gases
Closely packed molecules	Loosely packed molecules	Very loosely packed molecules

Fig. 3.8 Arrangement of molecules in solids, liquids and gases

Recall

- Matter is anything that has mass and occupies space.
- Matter can exist in three physical states, i.e., solid, liquid or gas.

- Solids, liquids and gases have distinguishable properties.
- Matter is made up of small particles called molecules.
- The arrangement of molecules in the three states of matter is different and hence this is responsible for their distinguishable properties.

 Let's Answer

1. Name one place where you will not find matter.
2. Name the form of matter that occupies space and has a definite shape.
3. Name the states of matter that make up our universe.
4. Classify the following substances according to the state in which they exist: iron nails, glycerine, oxygen, chocolate syrup, methane, acetylene, rubber, paper.
5. Name the state of matter in which the molecules are far apart.
6. Name a substance which can exist in three different states of matter.
7. Fill in the following tables:
   (a) Different materials used to make the same object:

S.No.	Object	Materials
1.	Door	Glass, iron, aluminium, wood, plastic
2.		
3.		
4.		
5.		

   (b) Visit your kitchen and observe your mother cooking different dishes using more than one material.

S.No.	Dish	Materials
1.	Fried Dal	Pulses, oil, water, salt, chilli, turmeric
2.		
3.		
4.		
5.		

8. Draw the arrangement of molecules in (a) lemon juice (b) soapcake (c) air that you blow on a window pane.

PHYSICAL PROPERTIES OF MATTER

The physical properties of matter are the characteristics which help us to distinguish matter of one kind from another. Here we shall discuss some important physical properties of matter.

Colour   Different substances have different colours. Some are colourless while others have specific colours. For example, water is colourless, iodine solution is violet, common salt is white, carbon (coal) is black, etc.

Odour   Matter can often be distinguished on the basis of smell or odour. Odour may be pleasant or unpleasant, sweet or pungent, and so on. Oxygen is odourless but gases such as hydrogen sulphide (rotten egg smell) and cooking gas have a characteristic smell or odour. Water has no smell but kerosene has a typical smell.

State   Matter can exist as a solid, liquid or gas. A solid substance may be *crystalline* (having a definite geometrical shape) or *amorphous* (exist as powder or lumps which have no definite geometrical shape). Sugar, salt, naphthalene, etc., are crystalline solids, whereas, clay, talc, wax, etc., are amorphous.

Taste   Different substances have different tastes. They may be tasteless like water, sweet like sugar, salty like common salt, or sour like vinegar and tamarind.

Solubility   Matter may be *soluble* (salt, sugar, etc., are soluble in water) or *insoluble* (wax, paper, etc., are insoluble in water) in a particular liquid. If the matter is soluble it is said to be *miscible* and if insoluble, it is termed *immiscible*.

 Activity 7

To observe the difference in solubility of various substances in water.

Materials required   Five test tubes, water, sodium chloride (common salt), sand, chalk powder, coconut oil, a drop of ink.

Method   Take the test tubes and fill half of each with water.

Take four of the test tubes and add sodium chloride, sand, chalk powder and a drop of ink, respectively, into them. To the fifth test tube add a drop of coconut oil. You will find that salt and ink are soluble in water but oil, sand and chalk powder are insoluble. So you have classified the materials taken, on the basis of their solubility in water (Fig. 3.9).

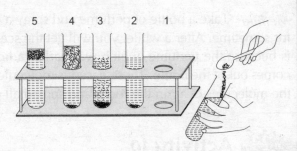

Fig. 3.9   Test for solubility of different substances

Similarly, some gases may be soluble in water and some insoluble. For example, gases such as oxygen and carbon dioxide are soluble in water. These dissolved gases are used by aquatic plants and animals for life processes such as photosynthesis and respiration. Gases such as methane and nitrogen are insoluble in water.

Transparency   Matter can be classified as *opaque* or *transparent*. Materials through which we can see are *transparent*, e.g., glass, water, air, etc. Materials such as wood, fog, or a metal sheet do not allow us to see through them. They are termed *opaque*.

 ## Activity 8

To observe the transparency of water and sand.

Materials required   Two clean glass tumblers, water, sand, two pieces of white paper, a marker.

Method   Write the letter 'A' on both the pieces of white paper. Now place them under the two glass tumblers. You will observe that the letter is visible through both the tumblers. Now add water in one tumbler and sand in the other. The letter 'A' is visible through the tumbler containing water but it can no longer be seen through the tumbler containing sand. Thus, clean water is transparent but sand is not.

Diffusion   Diffusion is the process of spreading of molecules of one substance among the molecules of another substance. The different states of matter can diffuse.

 ## Activity 9

To observe diffusion in gases.

Materials required   A bottle of perfume.

Method   Take a bottle of perfume and spray a little of it in one corner of the room. Wait for sometime. After a while, you will get the scent of the perfume in the entire room. This is because the perfume, which was earlier a liquid, changes to vapour (or gas), when it comes out of the bottle. These gaseous molecules of the perfume, now diffuse or mix with the molecules of air in the room and spread all over. Thus, we see that gases can diffuse.

 ## Activity 10

To observe diffusion in liquids.

Materials required   A dropper, glass beaker, red ink, water.

(Contd.)

Method Take a glass beaker and fill half of it with water. Now with the help of a dropper, add a few drops of red ink to the water and observe. What happens? (Fig. 3.10).

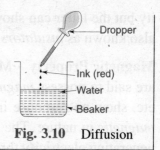

Fig. 3.10 Diffusion

Both ink and water are liquids. It is observed in the above activity that the ink gradually spreads out and mixes with water. Here, the molecules of ink mix with the molecules of water in the beaker. This is an example of diffusion.

Thus, in the case of liquids,

Diffusion is the spreading of the molecules of a liquid among the molecules of another liquid.

Conduction of Heat Matter in liquid and solid form can either be a good conductor of heat or a bad conductor of heat. Matter in gaseous form is generally a bad conductor of heat. For example, air is a bad conductor of heat. It is for this reason that air prevents heat from going out into the surroundings in winter through the layers of clothes of woollen fibres.

Activity 11

To demonstrate the conduction of heat in wood and in metals.

Materials required A glass beaker, water, two spatula (one made of metal and the other of wood), bunsen burner.

Method Take a glass beaker and fill it half with water. Now heat it till the water in it is sufficiently hot. Take it off the bunsen burner and dip the two spatula in hot water. After two minutes, if you touch the spatula one by one, you will feel that the spatula made of metal is hot, while that of wood is not so.

Thus, in metals heat flows from one end to another much faster than in wood. So, wood is a bad conductor while metal is a good conductor of heat.

Conduction of Electricity Matter can be classified on the basis of conductivity of electricity. Metals, as we all know, are good conductors of electricity. It is for this reason that electric wires and cables are made of copper. Air and water are bad conductors of electricity but the latter can show conductivity if it contains dissolved salts. Bad conductors are also known as *insulators*.

Magnetic Property Materials such as iron, nickel and cobalt respond to a magnet and are said to possess *magnetic* properties. Substances such as paper, wood, stainless steel, etc. show no response in the presence of a magnetic field, so they are said to be *non-magnetic* in nature. The magnetic property of iron makes it of the utmost importance in generating electricity through a dynamo, which is made of iron.

 Recall

* Matter possesses physical properties like transparency, diffusion, solubility, magnetic property, conductivity of heat and electricity, etc.
* Matter can be classified on the basis of its characteristic properties.

EXERCISES

1. **Choose the appropriate answer**

   (i) A substance has no fixed shape but has a fixed volume. Therefore, its physical state is
       (a) solid   (b) gaseous
       (c) liquid   (d) none of the above

   (ii) Perceiving the aroma of food being cooked in the kitchen while sitting in the study room is due to
       (a) diffusion   (b) evaporation
       (c) solubility   (d) the magnetic response

   (iii) In fire extinguishers carbon dioxide exists as a
       (a) solid   (b) liquid under pressure
       (c) gas   (d) none of the above

   (iv) Air is
       (a) opaque   (b) transparent
       (c) both (a) and (b)   (d) none of the above

   (v) A substance that is soluble in water is said to be
       (a) immiscible   (b) miscible
       (c) sparingly soluble   (d) none of the above

   (vi) Handles of cooking utensils, plastic articles and electrical switches are
       (a) good conductors of heat   (b) good conductors of electricity
       (c) bad conductors of heat   (d) bad conductors of heat and electricity

2. Match the following

Column A	Column B
(a) Diffusion	(i) Do not have definite shape but have fixed volume
(b) Matter	(ii) Spreading of particles
(c) Liquids	(iii) Occupies space and has mass
(d) Cobalt	(iv) Wood
(e) Opaque	(v) Magnetic material

3. Fill in the blanks

(a) A material which is a bad conductor of electricity is called a/an _____.

(b) Substances are classified on the basis of _____ and _____.

(c) Gases do not have definite _____ and _____.

(d) In a junk yard, a _____ is used to separate out iron articles.

(e) _____ is used to make thermometers.

4. Answer the following questions briefly

(a) What is classification? Why is it essential to classify things?

(b) In which state of matter are the molecules (a) closest together (b) farthest from each other?

(c) When a girl who has put on perfume walks past, we can smell perfume in the air though the amount of perfume used is very less. Explain why.

(d) State two features in which coal differs from mercury.

(e) In Figure 3.11, jar A contains a red gas and jar B contains colourless air. What will happen when the glass plate between them is pulled away? What is the name of this process?

(f) Why can we smell food cooking in the kitchen even when we are in another part of the house?

(g) Iron is used to make door latches, stickers, etc. Why?

(h) Identify and state the characteristics of the three states of matter represented in Figure 3.12.

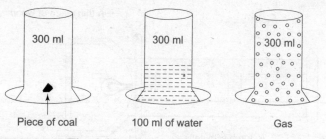

Fig. 3.12 Three forms of matter

(i) Water is a bad conductor of electricity, but still it is advised to keep hands dry while operating electrical appliances.

(j) Name the state of matter that diffuses the fastest.

(k) You are provided with two test tubes, A and B (Fig. 3.13). Both the test tubes contain water. In test tube A glycerine is added and in test tube B mustard oil.

   (i) What will you observe in test tubes A and B?

   (ii) Identify and state the property of matter involved in the above experiment.

   (iii) State the reason for the observations made in test tubes A and B.

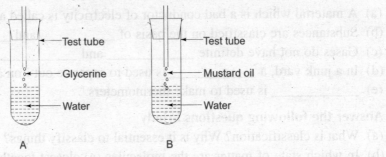

Fig. 3.13

(l) List five opaque and five transparent articles.

(m) Why is it more difficult to hold a hot stainless steel glass than a thermocol cup containing a hot liquid.

(n) Name a metal, other than copper, that is used to make electrical transmission wires.

THINK AND ANSWER

1. Why do you wear woollen clothes in winter?

2. Reena has a torch loaded with cells. On pressing the button it lights up. Out of curiosity, she opens the torch and places a rubberband, a piece of plastic bag, a thin piece of wood, a piece of aluminium foil, one by one between the cells and the bulb as shown in the figure below.

What will Reena observe and infer from this activity?

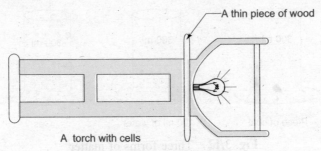

Fig. 3.14   A torch with cells

3. Rahul while playing cricket in the sun, happens to touch the top of a car (during fielding). He discovers that the car is extremely hot but the ball in his hand is cold. Explain why the body of the car is hot while the ball is cold.

Teacher's Notes

- A teacher can introduce the concept of classification by asking the students to separate out as boys and girls. She can then ask the boys and girls to segregate on the basis of their height, or length of their hair, or colour of their hair, etc.
- The three physical states of matter can be explained by asking students to collect solid, liquid and gaseous substances in their classroom.
- The properties of matter like solubility, transparency, magnetic response, shape, etc., could be taught by making use of articles such as water, a window pane, a duster, etc. which may be available in the classroom or in the laboratory.

4

- Pure substances and mixtures
- Separation of mixtures
- Methods of separation

Separation of Substances

Most of the things around us like air, sea water, solid rock, milk, tea, ink, paints, etc., are mixtures. A mixture is a substance that is made up of two or more substances. For example, air is made up of several gases (such as oxygen, nitrogen, carbon dioxide, etc.), water vapour and dust particles. Often, the mixtures need to be separated or purified before they can be used. For example, the tea that we drink is initially a mixture of water, milk, tea leaves, and sugar. But, we need to filter the tea before drinking to separate out the tea leaves.

In this chapter we shall study everything related to mixtures, starting from their formation to their separation into their constituents.

PURE SUBSTANCES AND MIXTURES

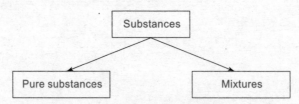

There are innumerable substances or materials around us, occurring either as a solid, liquid or gas. Substances can occur in two forms, namely, *pure* or *mixed*.

Pure Substance

A pure substance consists of a single substance with nothing else added to it. Substances such as iron, aluminium and water can occur in their pure state. When these are observed closely, it is seen that pure iron is composed only of iron atoms, distilled water contains only water molecules and pure aluminium contains only aluminium atoms.

Characteristics of Pure Substances

How can we identify the purity of a given substance? A pure substance has the following characteristics:

1. A pure substance is made up of only one kind of molecules. For example, all molecules in a lump of pure sugar, or in a sample of pure common salt are the same. But the molecules of sugar and salt are different.
2. No further separation of its components is possible by physical methods of separation such as filtration, distillation, crystallization, etc.
3. A pure substance has a definite set of properties like boiling point (in case of a liquid) or melting point (in case of a solid). The melting point of ice is 0 °C but if there is any impurity in it, such as common salt, then the melting point would be lowered to a value below 0 °C. Similarly, the boiling point of water is 100 °C, but if common salt is added to it, then it boils at a temperature above 100 °C. Thus, the addition of any impurity to a pure substance alters the properties of the latter.

Mixtures

A mixture is a substance which contains at least two substances mixed together in equal or varying proportions.

The substances constituting a mixture are called the *components* or *constituents* of the mixture. The components of a mixture can be separated by making use of the differences in the properties of these components. For example, iron and sulphur, when mixed together, form a mixture that retains the properties of both iron and sulphur. They can, therefore, be separated by physical methods. Sea water is a mixture containing salts dissolved in water. Common salt that is used in our kitchens is prepared from sea water.

Characteristics of a Mixture

A mixture has the following properties:

1. A mixture may be a solid, liquid or gas.
2. The components or constituents of a mixture can be separated by physical methods like filtration, evaporation, distillation, sublimation, etc.
3. The components of a mixture do not lose their properties on mixing.
4. The components of a mixture may be mixed in any ratio, but no new substance is formed, as no chemical reaction occurs.

Some examples of mixtures are described below.

(a) A glass of squash is a mixture of squash, water and sugar.

(b) Cooking gas is a mixture of gases.

(c) Mist is a mixture of water vapour in air.

(d) Smoke is a mixture of solid carbon particles in air.

(e) Rock salt is a mixture of salt and sand.

(f) Milk is a mixture of butter and water.

(g) Oil and water, and water and spirit are mixtures of liquids.

(h) Aerated drinks are a mixture of gas (usually carbon dioxide), water and sugar along with flavours and colours.

 Recall

- All materials around us can exist in two forms, i.e., in the pure state or as mixtures.
- A pure substance may be a solid, liquid or gas. It is always made up of only one kind of molecules.
- A mixture is made up of two or more components.
- The components of a mixture may be present in any ratio and they retain their individual properties.

 Let's Answer

1. Complete the following table:

Mixture	States of matter involved	Contents
air		
sea		
brass		
salad dressing		
soil		

2. Explain the differences between a pure substance and a mixture with examples.

3. Classify the following as pure substances or mixtures:

   (i) Fog   (ii) Gold   (iii) Oxygen   (iv) Muddy water

   (v) Hair cream   (vi) Smoke

(Contd.)

4. Fill in the blanks:

A _____ substance is made up of a single component. Gold is a soft metal, and is made _____ when other metals like copper, nickel, palladium and zinc are added to it. This is a _____ called alloy.

SEPARATION OF MIXTURES

From the examples discussed, we can conclude that a mixture has two or more substances in it. Since these substances retain their properties, it is possible to separate the various substances that make up a mixture. For example, before cooking rice, your mother sometimes picks out the grit and husk mixed with the rice. This is known as separation of a mixture. Thus,

Separation of a mixture is the process of isolating or taking apart the substances that make up the mixture.

Removing butter from milk is an example of separating the constituents of a mixture. Preparation of common salt by evaporation of sea water involves the separation of the salt from sea water. Straining out tea leaves from tea with the help of a strainer is also an example of separation.

Need to Separate the Constituents of a Mixture

The constituents of a mixture may need to be separated for the following purposes:
1. to retain any useful constituent of a mixture.
2. to get rid of any harmful component or constituent of a mixture.
3. to obtain a pure sample of a substance.

METHODS OF SEPARATION

So far we have discussed various types of mixtures that we come across in our daily life. At times it is essential to separate the constituents of a mixture to obtain a desired component, or to remove a harmful one. The separation is made possible because of the differences in properties of the different constituents. Generally, differences in physical properties such as solubility, boiling point, etc., are used. Following are the common methods of separation:

(a) Winnowing
(b) Hand-picking
(c) Magnetic separation
(d) Decantation
(e) Loading
(f) Use of separating funnel

(g) Filtration (h) Centrifugation
 (i) Evaporation (j) Crystallization
(k) Sublimation (l) Distillation

Winnowing

It is a technique in which the mixture is made to fall from a height and during this process, the lighter substances are separated by the wind. For example, separation of a mixture of wheat and husk is possible by this process. The wind carries the husk with it, which collects in a separate heap at a distance from the heap of wheat (Fig. 4.1). Winnowing is used at home and also in flour mills to separate out lighter components from wheat and rice.

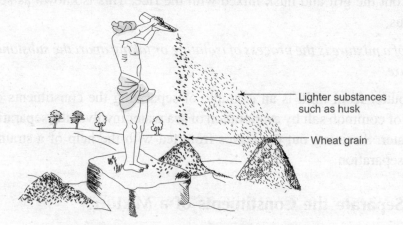

Lighter substances such as husk

Wheat grain

Fig. 4.1 Winnowing

Hand-Picking

As the term suggests, in this process the undesirable component is separated by hand. This method is only possible if the undesired component is present in small quantity. For example, grit or small pieces of stone are removed by hand from wheat, rice and pulses (Fig. 4.2).

Small pieces of stone or grit

Fig. 4.2 Hand-picking

Sieving

This method is used to separate the components of a mixture which vary in size. Even similar objects of different sizes can be separated by this method. For example, separation of cashewnuts of different sizes in the cashewnut industry. You must have seen your mother sieving flour to remove the unwanted substances in it before kneading. During the construction of buildings, a mixture of sand and gravel is separated using appropriate sieves. Grains are also sieved by this method to remove grit and husk from them. In the market, sieves with holes of different sizes are available (Fig. 4.3).

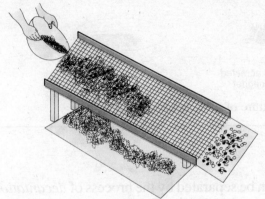

Fig. 4.3 Sieving

Magnetic Separation

Garbage is a mixture of paper, glass, aluminium, iron, other metals, plastic, and many other unwanted things. Nowadays, most of these items are recycled to be used again. Now, if we want to separate iron from this heap, we can utilize the magnetic property of iron. Iron is a substance that gets attracted towards a magnet. So cranes fitted with electromagnets are used to separate iron from other substances (Fig. 4.4).

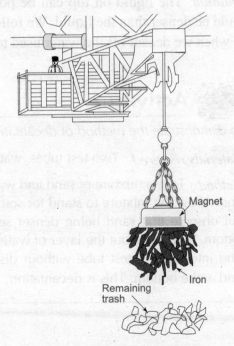

Fig. 4.4 Magnetic separation

Activity 1

To demonstrate the magnetic method of separation.

Materials required   Iron filings, sand, magnet.

Method   Make a mixture of the iron filings and sand and place it in a dish. How will you separate them? Bring a magnet near the mixture. The iron filings are attracted by the magnet and can be removed from the mixture. Sand remains in the dish. (Fig. 4.5)

| Sand and iron filings | Iron filings attracted by the magnet | Sand |

Fig. 4.5   Separation of a mixture of sand and iron filings

Decantation

A mixture of a liquid and an insoluble solid can be separated by the process of *decantation*. In this, the insoluble solid is allowed to settle under gravity, the process being called *sedimentation*. The liquid on top can be poured off or *decanted*. In this method, the solid should be denser than the liquid. We follow this process of decantation even in our kitchens when we decant off the water used to wash rice and pulses before cooking.

Activity 2

To demonstrate the method of decantation.

Materials required   Two test tubes, water, sand.

Method   Take a mixture of sand and water in a test tube. Allow the mixture to stand for sometime. You will observe that sand being denser settles at the bottom. Now pour out the layer of water above the sand into another test tube without disturbing the sand at the bottom. This is decantation.

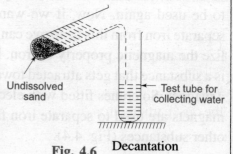

Undissolved sand

Test tube for collecting water

Fig. 4.6   Decantation

Loading

Water containing suspended particles, like that of clay, is not fit for drinking. It needs to be purified before it can be made available for drinking. This can be achieved by the process of *loading* in which alum is added to muddy water to allow the suspended clay particles to settle down. Alum helps in clumping the clay particles to form larger particles, thereby making them heavy and allowing them to settle at the bottom.

 Activity 3

To demonstrate the method of loading.

Materials required A glass beaker, muddy water, potash alum piece, a 20 cm thread.

Method Take a beaker and fill it half with muddy water. Tie a small piece of potash alum (phitkari) at one end of the thread and put it in the muddy water. Now shake the contents of the beaker by moving this piece of alum in circular motion. Then remove the alum and keep the beaker in that position for sometime. You will observe that the clay particles, which made the water appear muddy, have settled at the bottom. This is due to the alum that dissolves easily in water, thereby allowing the dirt particles to get loaded and become heavier. As a result, they slowly settle down at the bottom of the breaker.

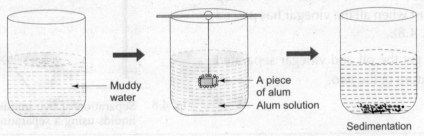

Muddy water

A piece of alum

Alum solution

Sedimentation

Fig. 4.7 Loading of suspended particles by using alum

 Do You Know?

Why do we often sprinkle water before sweeping a dusty room? This is done to prevent the dust particles from rising above the floor. Here, water is used to *load* the dust particles.

Separating Funnel

Liquids which mix well with each other are said to be *miscible* and those which do not mix are said to be *immiscible*.

The process of decantation can be used to separate two immiscible liquids by using a separating funnel or a burette. For example, water and oil are two immiscible liquids which can be separated by this process. Similarly, a mixture of oil and vinegar can be separated by this method. The two immiscible liquids form two different layers. The one that is denser will form the lower layer which separates out first on opening the stopcock of the separating funnel.

 ## Activity 4

To separate a mixture of two liquids using a separating funnel.

Materials required Glass beaker, separating funnel, oil, vinegar.

Method Take a mixture of oil and vinegar and pour it into a separating funnel with its tap closed. You will see two separate layers of liquids with the oil floating over vinegar. When the tap of the funnel is opened, vinegar runs down into the beaker first. The tap is closed just when all the vinegar has passed down (Fig. 4.8).

Thus, you get the oil and vinegar separated from a mixture of the two.

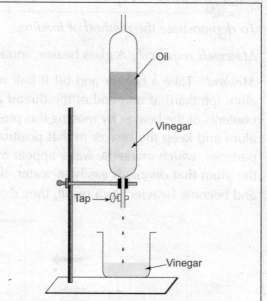

Fig. 4.8 Separation of two immiscible liquids using a separating funnel

Filtration

This method is used for separating a solid from a liquid in which it has not dissolved. For example, tea contains tea leaves which can be separated by pouring tea through a strainer or a piece of cloth. The strainer has numerous small holes which are big enough to allow the liquid to pass through but retain the tea leaves (Fig. 4.9).

Fig. 4.9 Filtration of tea using a strainer

Let us take another example of a mixture in which there are tiny particles of grit and clay in water. These particles are insoluble in water and just keep floating in it. This type of mixture is called a *suspension*. The particles can be removed by pouring the mixture through a filter paper. A filter paper has holes as in a tea strainer but they are much smaller.

Activity 5

To filter a mixture of clay and water.

Materials required A circular filter paper, funnel, conical flask, a glass rod, beaker, clay, water.

Method Fold the filter paper to form a cone. Fit the cone in a funnel and place the funnel on a conical flask. Hold the glass rod against the inner wall of the funnel and pour the suspension of clay and water on to the filter paper in the funnel (Fig. 4.10). What do you see on the filter paper? What do you see in the conical flask?

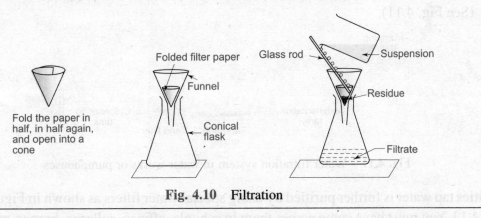

Fold the paper in half, in half again, and open into a cone

Folded filter paper

Funnel

Conical flask

Glass rod

Suspension

Residue

Filtrate

Fig. 4.10 Filtration

The filter paper looks dirty as all the clay and grit are held back by it. This is known as the *residue*. The water that trickles down into the conical flask is clear. This is known as the *filtrate*.

Thus, *the solid component of a mixture that cannot pass through the filter paper and collects on it is known as the residue of filtration, and the liquid component that passes out through the filter paper is known as the filtrate.*

Water in swimming pools is regularly filtered. Urban sewage and farm waste rich in organic matter need to be treated or filtered before being discharged into rivers or into the sea. This is achieved by using large metallic meshes which retain the residue and prevent the blocking of drains.

In our cities the concerned authorities need to take up the availability of clean, drinking water as a priority, for water contaminated with suspended solids and micro-organisms can cause water-borne diseases like cholera, typhoid, dysentry, etc. Water, before reaching the taps in our homes covers the journey on the ground as it flows in streams and rivers, where it comes in contact with many dissolved substances, sediments of clay and grit. It may even contain harmful bacteria.

The water supplied needs to be treated to make it fit for drinking. The main stages of the treatment are:

1. *Sedimentation*   Lime and alum are added and the suspended solids are allowed to settle in sedimentation tanks. These chemicals help in clumping the particles into larger particles, which settle on standing as shown in Figure 4.11.

2. *Filtration*   After sedimentation, the water is filtered through beds of sand. This removes some solid particles and certain harmful micro-organisms.

3. *Addition of chemicals*   The water is aerated to remove unpleasant odour. Finally, chlorine is added to water to destroy the micro-organisms left behind. A small amount of lime is also added to make water alkaline to prevent the rusting of iron water pipes (See Fig. 4.11).

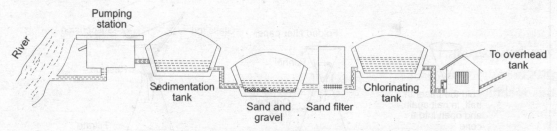

Fig. 4.11   Water filtration system in water works or pumphouses

In cities tap water is further purified by using special water filters as shown in Figures 4.12 and 4.13. You must have come across them in schools, offices, colleges, homes, etc. Some common household purifiers are ceramic candle filters, resin- and iodine-based purifiers. These enable us to get rid of impurities in water.

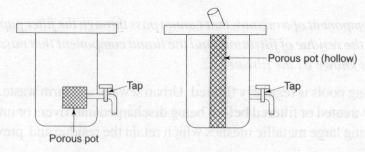

Fig. 4.12   Water purifiers used at home

Nowadays, electric water purifiers (like the ultraviolet purifier) are also available to us. These not only filter out the dust and destroy micro-organisms but also double-check the contamination level of water before allowing it out for consumption.

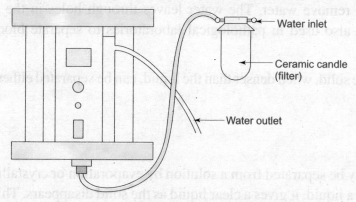

Fig. 4.13   Electrical (modern) water purifier

Centrifugation

This method is used to remove floating impurities in a liquid. It is impossible to filter out very tiny particles, since they clog up the holes of the filter paper and make the filtering process very slow. Therefore, the process of centrifugation is preferred over filtration. In this technique, the mixture is put into a small tube, which is put into the centrifuge machine, as shown in Figure 4.14.

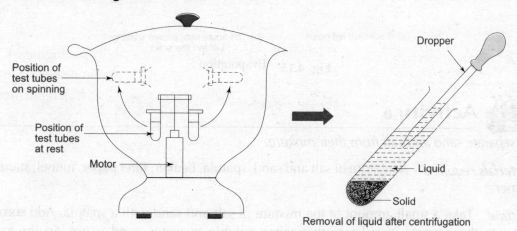

Fig. 4.14   A centrifuge

When the machine is switched on, the test tube inside spins at a high speed and the solid in the mixture is flung to the bottom of the test tube. After centrifugation, the liquid is drawn off with a dropper, as shown in the diagram. This process is also used in milk dairies, to separate cream from milk. Cream, being lighter than milk, collects at the centre and floats over the mixture. Even the household mixer, and washing machines, work on this principle. In a washing machine, wet clothes are spun around at high speed at the end of a washing cycle to remove water. The water leaves through holes in the washing drum. Centrifugation is also used in pathological laboratories to separate blood cells from a blood sample.

Thus, an insoluble solid, when denser than the liquid, can be separated either by decantation or centrifugation.

Evaporation

A soluble salt may be separated from a solution by evaporation or crystallization. When a solid dissolves in a liquid, it gives a clear liquid as the solid disappears. This clear liquid is called a *solution*. Sea water and sugar solution are good examples of solutions.

The solid can be separated from the solution if it is left open in the air in a warm place. The liquid turns into vapour—it evaporates, leaving the solid behind (Fig. 4.15). To hasten the process of evaporation, the solution may also be boiled. This method is used on a large-scale to obtain common salt from sea water or lake water containing common salt.

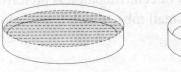 

(a) A solution left open (b) The liquid evaporates leaving behind the solid

Fig. 4.15 Evaporation

 Activity 6

To separate sand and salt from their mixture.

Materials required A mixture of salt and sand, spatula, beaker, filter paper, funnel, stand, burner.

Method Take a small amount of the mixture of salt and sand with a spatula. Add some water to the mixture. You know that salt is soluble in water, sand is not. So the salt dissolves in water and forms a solution and the sand is left behind. A part of the sand settles down at the bottom. Filter off the rest of the mixture. So we get back the sand, as sediment and as residue on the filter paper. The filtrate contains the salt solution.

(Contd...)

Now, in order to get back the salt from the salt solution, we have to evaporate the water from the salt solution. Pour the salt solution into an evaporating dish and heat it on the burner. The water from the solution evaporates, leaving behind the solid residue of the salt (Fig. 4.16).

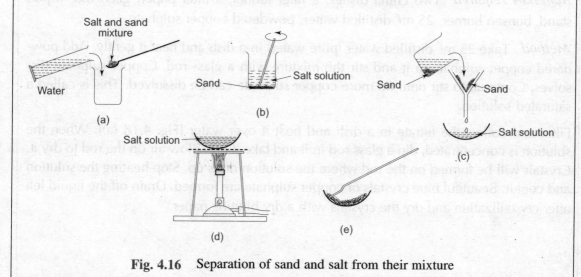

Fig. 4.16   Separation of sand and salt from their mixture

Crystallization

This method is used to obtain a purer product because certain impurities are left behind in a solution.

To obtain a pure sample of the substance, a large quantity of it is dissolved in a hot liquid. From time to time, a small sample of the solution is transferred to a test tube and cooled under a running tap. When the sample on cooling gives crystals, the whole solution is covered with a watch glass and left to cool (Fig. 4.17). Crystals are formed on cooling. Sugar, common salt and many other salts are purified by crystallization.

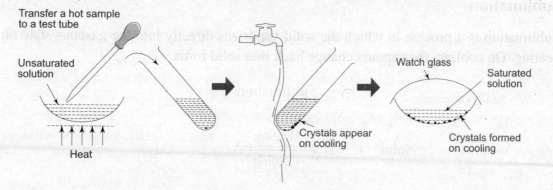

Fig. 4.17   Crystallization

Activity 7

To prepare crystals of copper sulphate.

Materials required Two china dishes, a filter funnel, a filter paper, glass rod, tripod stand, bunsen burner, 25 ml distilled water, powdered copper sulphate.

Method Take 25 ml distilled water (pure water) in a dish and heat it gently. Add powdered copper sulphate to it and stir the mixture with a glass rod. Copper sulphate dissolves. Continue to stir until no more copper sulphate can be dissolved. This is called a saturated solution.

Filter and collect the filtrate in a dish and heat it over water [Fig. 4.18 (a)]. When the solution is concentrated, dip a glass rod in it and take it out. Blow air on the rod to dry it. Crystals will be formed on the rod where the solution dries up. Stop heating the solution and cool it. Beautiful blue crystals of copper sulphate are formed. Drain off the liquid left after crystallization and dry the crystals with a dry blotting paper.

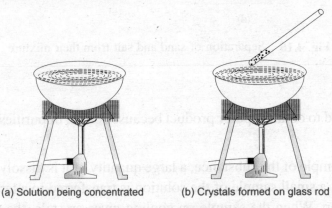

(a) Solution being concentrated   (b) Crystals formed on glass rod

Fig. 4.18   Crystallization

Sublimation

Sublimation is a process in which the solid vaporizes directly into the gaseous state on heating. On cooling, the vapours change back into solid form.

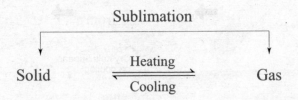

Examples of substances that are known to sub-limate are iodine, ammonium chloride, camphor, solid carbon dioxide (dry ice), etc.

Iodine can be purified by sublimation (Fig. 4.19). Take an evaporating dish and add impure iodine to it. Cover the impure iodine with an inverted funnel and heat it. The tip of the funnel is plugged with cotton to prevent the iodine vapours from escaping. Vapours of iodine on cooling condense on the cooler parts of the funnel as fine crystals.

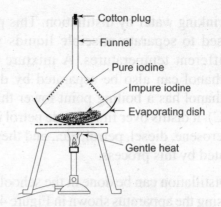

Fig. 4.19 Purification of iodine by sublimation

 Activity 8

To separate the components of a mixture of ammonium chloride and salt.

Materials required Ammonium chloride, common salt, a china dish, a tripod stand, wire gauze, glass funnel, burner.

Method Take a teaspoonful of a mixture of ammonium chloride and common salt in a china dish. Place the china dish over a tripod stand. Cover the china dish with an inverted funnel and plug the opening in the funnel with cotton. Heat the dish till white fumes begin to evolve from the mixture. Stop heating and let it cool. On removing the funnel, you will see pure, white ammonium chloride deposited on the upper, cooler parts of the funnel. Salt is left behind in the china dish (Fig. 4.20).

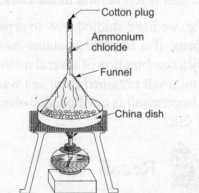

Fig. 4.20 Separation of ammonium chloride and salt by sublimation

Distillation

Distillation is a process of obtaining pure liquid from a solution. It is actually a combination of evaporation and condensation, i.e.,

Distillation = Evaporation + Condensation

The solution is heated in order to vaporize the liquid. The vapours of the liquid on cooling, condense into pure liquid. For example, sea water in many countries is converted into drinking water by distillation. This process is also used to separate miscible liquids which boil at different temperatures. A mixture of water and ethanol can also be separated by distillation. As ethanol has a boiling point lower than water (100 °C), it distils over first. Crude petrol is a mixture of kerosene, diesel, petrol, etc., and they can be separated by this process.

Distillation can be done in the school laboratory by using the apparatus shown in Figure 4.21. If we take salt water in a conical flask and heat it, the water vapour will rise and slowly move out through the delivery tube. On reaching the test tube, whose walls

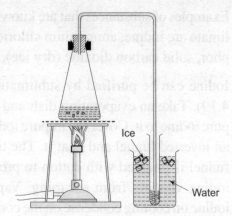

Fig. 4.21 Distillation of salt water to get pure water

are cooled by the ice water surrounding it, the hot water vapour condenses to form droplets of water. These droplets collect in the test tube as pure water which is not at all salty to taste. Salt is left behind in the flask.

So far, we have studied how to separate a mixture containing two components. But what happens, if a mixture contains more than two components? In such cases, we need to apply a combination of several methods of separation to achieve our purpose. For example, common salt obtained from sea water is impure. It is purified by using various methods. The impure salt is crushed, dissolved in water, filtered, evaporated, and crystallized to get pure salt.

 Recall

- Separation is needed to remove, say, any unwanted or harmful components of a mixture.
- The constituents of a mixture can be separated by physical methods like filtration, distillation, etc.
- Selection of the method of separation depends upon the nature of the component to be separated.
- Various methods of separation include winnowing, hand-picking, sieving, centrifugation, crystallization, sublimation, decantation, filtration, evaporation, and distillation.
- Sometimes, a mixture has to be separated by employing more than one of the listed methods of separation.

EXERCISES

1. **Choose the appropriate answer**
   (i) Camphor is separated from common salt by
      (a) distillation   (b) sublimation
      (c) evaporation   (d) filtration

(ii) Peanuts are separated from a mixture of pulses and rice by
    (a) sieving   (b) winnowing
    (c) hand-picking   (d) all of the above

(iii) A liquid is obtained from a solution by
    (a) sublimation   (b) distillation
    (c) crystallization   (d) none of above

(iv) Two immiscible liquids are separated by
    (a) filtration   (b) a separating funnel
    (c) evaporation   (d) distillation

(v) A mixture of iodine and salt is separated by
    (a) sieving   (b) crystallization
    (c) sublimation   (d) evaporation

2. Fill in the blanks

If _____ salt is to be _____ from a mixture of _____ and small stones, water is added to the mixture and _____. The _____ salt dissolves and forms a _____. The _____ sand and stones, do not do so. The _____ is then filtered. Sand and stones are held back by the filter paper and are called the _____. The _____ is salt solution. When it is evaporated, _____ of salt are left behind.

3. Match the following

Column A	Column B
(i) To remove foreign particles from a substance	(a) Sublimation
(ii) A liquid in which other substances are dissolved	(b) Separating funnel
	(c) Solution
(iii) To separate volatile liquids from solutions	(d) Solvent
	(e) Fractional distillation
(iv) To remove denser insoluble solids like cream from milk	(f) Purify
	(g) Residue
(v) To separate immiscible liquids	(h) Centrifugation
(vi) To separate solid carbon dioxide and salt	(i) Hand-picking
(vii) To separate solids on the basis of variable sizes	(j) Sieving

4. List and draw the apparatus you would use for the following experiments

(i) Purification of sea water or a mixture of ethanol and water
(ii) Separation of a mixture of water and oil
(iii) Separation of sand and salt
(iv) Purification of dirty water
(v) Separation of butter from milk

5. Copy out the following table and write an example of a mixture in each empty box.

For example, coffee is a mixture of a solid and a liquid. Try to find examples that have not been used earlier:

	Solid	Liquid	Gas
Solid		coffee	
Liquid			
Gas			

6. **Mention the property on which the separation of the following mixtures would be based**
   (a) Mixture of husk and wheat.
   (b) Mixture of vinegar and oil.
   (c) Mixture of ammonium chloride and salt.
   (d) To obtain diesel from crude oil.
   (e) Crystals of zinc from zinc and dilute sulphuric acid.

7. **Define**
   (a) A pure substance
   (b) Sublimation
   (c) Loading
   (d) Separation of mixture

8. **Answer the following in brief**
   (a) To purify common salt, which technique would you follow—evaporation or crystallization and why?
   (b) Rajan has a scrapyard. His friend Adwait brings in a load of iron mixed with aluminium. How will Rajan separate the iron from aluminium?
   (c) How will you separate a mixture of sand, copper sulphate and iron?
   (d) Why is it essential to separate a mixture into its constituents?

THINK AND ANSWER

1. A mixture contains two liquids A and B. Liquid A has a boiling point of 80°C and liquid B has a boiling point of 140°C. The mixture is heated in a flask. Draw the apparatus, label it and explain the procedure, stating which liquid will boil off first.
2. Suppose a ship gets wrecked on an island in the Pacific ocean. The passengers, however, manage to bring plenty of firewood, match boxes and some pots ashore. Describe, with the help of diagrams, how the passengers can obtain drinking water from the salty ocean water.
3. How will you separate a mixture of sodium chloride, camphor and chalk?

 Teacher's Notes

- The teacher can explain properties of a pure substance and a mixture by taking the example of common salt and an aerated drink.
- Many methods of separating mixtures described in the text can be demonstrated in the class. Else, the students may be asked to perform the activities themselves (except distillation).

5

- Different types of changes
- Comparison of physical and chemical changes
- Absorption and evolution of energy in a change

Changes Around Us

Almost everything in this universe undergoes some change or the other. Changes like burning of wood, glowing of an electric bulb, growth of a tree, evaporation of water, rising and setting of the sun, change of seasons, souring of milk, spoilage of food, ripening of fruit, etc., are common to us. Some of these changes are beneficial to us and some are not. All the changes occurring around us are due to some reason or the other and thus, it becomes essential for us to study the mechanism of the changes, and factors influencing the same.

DIFFERENT TYPES OF CHANGES

We see a variety of changes occurring around us. These changes may be classified into various categories, namely,

- Slow and fast
- Reversible and irreversible
- Periodic and non-periodic
- Desirable and undesirable
- Physical and chemical

Slow and Fast Changes

Slow changes are those which take place over a long period of time. Fermentation of sugar into alcohol, rusting of iron, change of seasons, growth of plants and animals, etc., are some examples of slow changes. Some of these changes occur in days and some in months or years.

Fast changes are those which take place quickly. These include flashes of lightning, burning of gas, melting of ice when placed on a heater, an electric light switched on or off, etc.

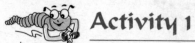

Activity 1

To observe a slow change and a fast change.

Materials required   A rubber band, iron nails.

Method   Take a rubber band and stretch it. You will see its shape changing and once you release it, the rubber band regains its shape.

Now take a few nails of iron and leave them in the open. After some days, you will observe a reddish-brown powder on them. This is nothing but rust and the change occurs when iron comes in contact with moist air.

Thus, the stretching and release of a rubber band is an example of a fast change and the rusting of iron is a slow change.

Reversible and Irreversible Changes

Reversible (temporary) changes are those changes which can be reversed, meaning that in these changes, the substance changed can be recovered in its original form. As we know, ice on heating melts into water and the same water can be converted back into ice on cooling. So melting of ice is a reversible change. This is also true of vaporization of water and sublimation of iodine.

Irreversible (permanent) changes are those which cannot be reversed. The new substance formed cannot be changed back into its original form. Burning of paper into ash, conversion of wheat into flour, growth of a plant, etc., are examples of permanent changes.

Recall

- Almost everything in the universe undergoes a change.
- Changes are of various kinds like slow and fast, reversible and irreversible, desirable and undesirable, physical and chemical, periodic and non-periodic.
- A slow change occurs over a long period of time, whereas a fast change occurs in minutes or seconds.
- The original substance can be recovered in a reversible change. This is not possible for an irreversible change.

Let's Answer

1. Mark the following sentences as true or false. If false, rewrite them:
   (i) Dispatching of a cricket ball by Tendulkar for a six is a slow change.

   _____

   (ii) Erasing the written contents of your notebook is a fast change.

   _____

   (iii) Clicking of a photograph is a slow change.

   _____

   (iv) Growing of a sapling into a plant is a fast change.

   _____

   (v) Spoiling of a pizza is a reversible change.

   _____

2. Fill in the blanks:
   (i) Burning of gasoline in the engine of your car is a _____.
   (ii) Melting of ice is a _____.
   (iii) Rahul having a choco-bar is a _____.
   (iv) Crashing of Columbia, the spacecraft carrying Kalpana Chawla was a _____.
   (v) Stretching of a rubber band is a _____.

Periodic and Non-Periodic Changes

Periodic changes are those changes that occur over and over again after fixed intervals. Periodic changes can also be called *cyclic changes*, as after the last change, the first one is repeated again. Ushering in of a day at sunrise and setting in of night at sunset is an example of a periodic change. Similarly, changing of seasons, changing phases of the moon, ticking of a clock, revolving of the earth around the sun in $365\frac{1}{4}$ days, occurrence of high and low tides in a sea are some common examples of periodic changes. Thus, periodic changes are predictable changes.

Non-periodic changes are those changes that do not occur after fixed intervals. It can also be said that non-periodic changes can occur at any time and are, therefore, non-predictable. For example, storms, earthquakes, cyclones, landslides, growth of plants and animals, etc., are changes that do not occur periodically. Since, non-periodic changes like earthquakes, landslides, storms, etc., cannot be foreseen, it becomes difficult to protect ourselves from their harmful effects. Scientists have been successful in predicting weather changes to some degree but need to work more on how to predict earthquakes and landslides in order to save valuable human lives.

Desirable and Undesirable Changes

Desirable changes are those changes which are beneficial to us. Cooking of food, conversion of milk to curd, growth of plants, change of seasons, sunrise, sunset, generation of electricity from water or air, etc., are some examples of desirable changes.

Undesirable changes are those changes which are harmful to us. Rotting of food, spoiling of fruits, vegetables or milk, crashing of aircrafts, cyclones, storms, etc., are examples of undesirable changes.

All the changes occurring around us are not desirable ones, but we should always speed up the desirable changes so that our earth is a better place to live in. We know that cutting of trees can cause serious climatic changes, so we should promote afforestation (desirable change) instead of deforestation (undesirable change). Sunderlal Bahugana was instrumental in starting the *Chipko Movement* in Garhwal to prevent deforestation there.

Scientists all over the globe are discouraging the use of pesticides and insecticides for growing plants as they are harmful to us.

Earlier, we used to preserve milk by boiling but now we store it in refrigerators. In order to prevent spoiling of milk by bacteria, it is pasteurized before it reaches the consumer. *Pasteurization is the process of heating milk to a high temperature and then suddenly cooling it, which kills the undesirable microbes*. This technique was first proposed by a French scientist, *Louis Pasteur*, and is therefore popularly known as *pasteurization*. Pasteurized milk is sold in the market in sealed tetrapacks in which it can stay fresh for many days and can be stored without refrigeration.

Sometimes, desirable and undesirable changes occur simultaneously. For example, burning of fuel in cars, buses, taxis, etc., is important as they are a major source of transportation but at the same time, it releases toxic substances in our environment which causes pollution. Pollution is a major problem in cities as it leads to various health problems like asthma, allergies, etc. The dam in Tehri has brought electricity to many areas but at the same time, it has destroyed Tehri as a town.

- Periodic change is a change that occurs at regular intervals.
- Non-periodic changes cannot be predicted.
- Desirable changes are good for us.
- Undesirable changes should be discouraged as they harm us.

Let's Answer

1. Fill in the blanks:
   (i) The departure of the 'Metro train' from Seelampur to Tis Hazari is a _____ change.
   (ii) Changes that are not predictable are called _____.
   (iii) All the changes around us are not _____ ones.
   (iv) Occurrence of a solar eclipse is a _____ change.
   (v) _____ change occurs at regular intervals.
   (vi) Rotation of the moon around the earth is a _____ change.
   (vii) The heartbeat of a human is a _____ change.
   (viii) Liberation of Afghanistan from the clutches of the Taliban is a _____ change for the people of Afghanistan.
2. Give two examples each of a desirable change and an undesirable change.
3. Mark the following sentences as true or false:
   (i) Occurrence of day and night is a periodic change.
   (ii) Flooding of rivers is a desirable change.
   (iii) Beating of the heart is an undesirable change.
   (iv) A class having six periods of chemistry in a week is a non-periodic change.

Physical and Chemical Changes

All changes can be broadly classified into physical and chemical changes.

Physical Change

Consider the following examples:
(a) Press the switch of an electric bulb. The bulb glows and gives out light and heat. Now switch it off. The bulb stops glowing. After sometime, if you touch the bulb, you will feel that it is no longer hot (Fig. 5.1).

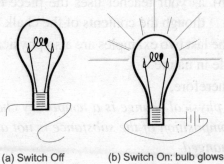

(a) Switch Off   (b) Switch On: bulb glows

Fig. 5.1 Example of a physical change

(b) Take some water in a beaker and add a teaspoon of salt to it. Stir well. The salt dissolves completely. Taste the solution. It will have a salty taste. Now heat the solution, until all the water evaporates. A white substance, salt, will be left behind in the beaker (Fig. 5.2).

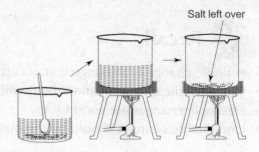

Fig. 5.2   Evaporation is a physical change

Let us now discuss the changes taking place in these examples.

In the two examples discussed:

- No new substances are formed.
- The changes are temporary and reversible. For example, in (a), the bulb stops glowing and cools down. In (b), the salt is recovered from its solution by a simple method, evaporation.
- In both the cases, the changes affect only the physical properties of the substance. For example,
  In (a), the filament in the bulb conducts electricity, gets heated up and emits light. It becomes white hot when emitting light and grey when cold.
  In (b), the salt dissolves in water and undergoes a change in its physical state without losing its characteristics.

Let us study some more examples:

(a) breaking of a bone china plate in the kitchen.

(b) use of a chalk by your teacher in class.

The above two examples are also examples of physical changes, where:

(a) upon breaking a bone china plate, the small pieces of the same cannot be joined to get the original plate, though the pieces are still made of the same substance as the bone china plate.

(b) as your teacher uses the piece of chalk on the blackboard it gets smaller in size, though the contents of the chalk in her hand and on the board are the same.

The last two examples are also physical changes but such physical changes are not reversible in nature.

Therefore,

A physical change is a temporary change in which no new substance is formed and the composition of the substance is not altered, although certain specific properties may be changed.

Examples of Physical Changes

Some common examples of physical change are:

- Melting of wax
- Melting of butter
- Formation of dew
- Heating of an iron rod

- Heating of platinum wire
- Melting of sulphur
- Precipitation of rain and snow
- Evaporation of water from lakes, rivers and oceans

 Activity 2

To show that condensation of steam is a physical change.

Materials required Beaker, 50 mℓ water, lid, burner.

Method Boil 50 mℓ water in a beaker. Water changes into steam. Hold a cold lid against the steam escaping from the beaker. What do you see on the underside? The steam condenses and droplets of water are seen on the lid (Fig. 5.3). What kind of a change is this?

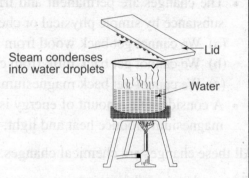

Steam condenses into water droplets — Lid

Water

Fig. 5.3 Condensation of steam

Steam condensing to water is a reversible change, with no new chemical substance being formed. Also, the water undergoes only a change in its physical state, i.e., liquid water changes to gas (steam) during the process. So, it is a physical change.

Chemical Change

Let us consider a few more changes taking place around us. You might have noticed that when seeds are sown in the earth, they grow into seedlings. After some days, the seedlings grow into plants. We cannot get back the seed from the plant. This means that the change is a permanent one. Also, we get a new product, the plant, which is entirely different from the starting material, i.e., the seed. We can say that the growth of a seed into a plant is a chemical change.

Consider the following examples:

(a) Burn a piece of wood using a match stick. Ash is left behind as residue (Fig. 5.4).
(b) Take some milk in a vessel and add a few drops of lime juice to it. Leave it undisturbed for a few hours. The milk changes into curd.

(c) Using a pair of tongs, take a piece of magnesium ribbon and heat it over a burner. It starts burning with a dazzling light and produces dense white fumes. The white fumes, on cooling, leave behind a white residue of magnesium oxide.

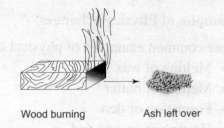

Wood burning   Ash left over

Fig. 5.4   Example of a chemical change

In examples (a), (b) and (c):

- New chemical substances having a composition and properties different from that of the original substance are formed: (a) wood changes to ash, (b) milk changes to curd, (c) magnesium changes to magnesium oxide.
- The changes are permanent and irreversible, i.e., we cannot get back the original substance by simple physical or chemical methods.
  (a) We cannot get back wood from ash.
  (b) We cannot get back milk from curd.
  (c) We cannot get back magnesium from magnesium oxide.
- A considerable amount of energy is evolved or absorbed, e.g., burning of wood and magnesium produce heat and light.

All these changes are chemical changes.

Thus, *a chemical change is a permanent change in which the original substance gives rise to one or more new substances, with a different composition and properties.*

Activity 3

To demonstrate a chemical change.

Materials required   Copper carbonate powder, test tube, burner.

Method   Heat a small quantity of copper carbonate in a test tube. The bluish-green powder turns black.

The black residue formed is copper oxide (Fig. 5.5). Cool the test tube for some time. Do we get back the bluish-green copper carbonate? No.

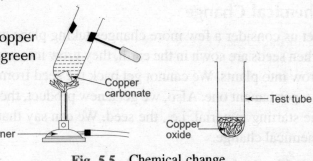

Fig. 5.5   Chemical change

$$\text{Copper carbonate} \xrightarrow{\text{heat}} \text{Copper oxide} + \text{Carbon dioxide} \uparrow$$

(bluish-green)   (black)

This activity shows that the formation of copper oxide from copper carbonate is an example of a *chemical reaction*. A chemical reaction is a chemical change which involves formation of a new substance or substances having different properties.

The substance present before a reaction is called the *reactant* and the new substance formed is called the *product*. Therefore heating of copper carbonate is a chemical change and the products are copper oxide and carbon dioxide. The properties and composition of the products are different from those of the reactant, copper carbonate.

Examples of Chemical Changes

Some common examples of chemical changes are:

- Conversion of milk to curd.
- Rusting of iron.
- Growth of a plant.
- Burning of paper, wood, kerosene, etc.
- Digestion of food.
- Fermentation of *idli* batter.

 Do You Know?

Burning of crackers is a chemical change. Crackers contain magnesium and other chemicals, which when lighted produce a violent chemical change. The reaction involved liberates energy in the form of heat, light and sound.

Fig. 5.6 Burning of crackers— a chemical change

Comparison of Physical and Chemical Changes

The differences between physical and chemical changes are mentioned in Table 5.1 below.

Table 5.1 Differences between physical and chemical changes

Physical Change	Chemical Change
1. This change is usually reversible and temporary.	1. This change is usually irreversible and permanent.
2. No new substance is formed.	2. New substances are formed.
3. Generally, no exchange of energy occurs.	3. Exchange of energy in the form of heat, light, etc., occurs.

 Recall

- Physical changes are usually reversible and temporary.
- No new substances are formed during a physical change.

- Physical changes affect only the physical properties of substances such as shape, size, state, etc., but do not alter their composition.
- Chemical changes are usually permanent and irreversible.
- New chemical substances with different composition and properties are formed.
- Considerable energy changes are involved.

Let's Answer

1. Choose the correct word or set of words:
   (i) Cooking *chapatis* is a *chemical change/physical change*.
   (ii) The substance present before a chemical reaction occurs is called a *product/reactant*.
   (iii) When Sourav takes a catch in the field, it is *a physical change/chemical change*.
   (iv) In a chemical change a new substance is *formed/not formed*.
   (v) When electricity is passed through water, hydrogen and oxygen are formed, whose properties are *similar/dissimilar* to that of water.

2. Fill in the blanks selecting words from the box below:

   - physical change
   - sublimation
   - fermentation
   - oxygen
   - baking soda
   - carbon dioxide
   - evaporation
   - chemical change
   - nitrogen

   While baking a cake, _____ is added to the cake batter or mixture. On keeping the mixture in an oven at the required temperature, the contents _____ due to the release of _____. The mixture is said to have _____. A new substance is formed during the process, so it is a _____ change.

3.

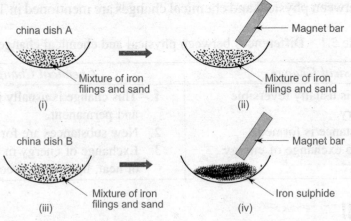

china dish A

Mixture of iron filings and sand

(i)

Magnet bar

Mixture of iron filings and sand

(ii)

china dish B

Mixture of iron filings and sand

(iii)

Magnet bar

Iron sulphide

(iv)

(Contd...)

You are provided with two china dishes, namely A and B as shown in the figures (i)—(ii). China dish A and B have iron filings and sand in them (Fig. (i) and (iii)).

(i) Draw the missing links in Figures (ii), (iii) and (iv).
(ii) State the type of change that you will observe in Figures (i) and (iii).
(iii) Are any new substances formed in Figures (ii) and (iv)?
(iv) Is there any energy change visible in Figures (i) and (iii)?

ABSORPTION AND EVOLUTION OF ENERGY

A change is usually associated with absorption (taking in) or evolution (giving out) of energy by the substances undergoing the change. This energy may be in any form, i.e., heat, light or sound.

We know that most of the chemical changes involve energy changes. Some physical changes are also accompanied by change in energy.

 ## Activity 4

To observe change in energy in a physical change.

Materials required A glass beaker, sugar, water, a burner, evaporating dish, stirrer.

Method Take a beaker and fill it half with water. To this, add sugar and heat the contents of the beaker. Energy is being supplied in the form of heat to dissolve the sugar in water. But no new substance has been formed.

The sugar present in water can be recovered from it by heating the contents of the beaker in an evaporating dish [See Fig. (5.7)].

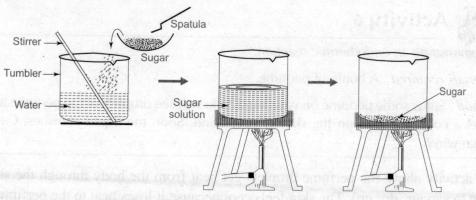

Fig. 5.7   Energy change in a physical change

 **Activity 5**

To observe change in energy in a chemical change.

Materials required A tin, quicklime, water.

Method Take a tin and fill it half with water. To this add a measured amount of quicklime, a white powder. You will notice that when quicklime comes in contact with water, the mixture gets heated up. This can be felt by touching the walls of the tin. A new substance, slaked lime, is formed that leads to the evolution of heat. See Figure 5.8.

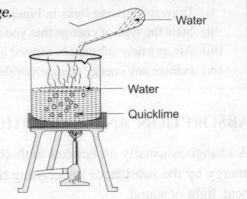
Water

Water

Quicklime

Quicklime + water ⟶ slaked lime + heat

Fig. 5.8 Liberation of heat during a chemical change

The activities discussed prove that for a change to occur, interaction between substances is essential and energy change is almost a must in any change.

Broadly speaking, there are two kinds of heat changes—*exothermic* and *endothermic*.

Exothermic changes are those changes during which heat is given out. For example, burning of wood, glowing of an electric lamp, dissolution of sodium hydroxide flakes in water, bursting of a cracker, etc.

Endothermic changes are those during which heat is absorbed. For example, melting of ice, cooking of food, drying of wet clothes, dissolution of ammonium chloride in water, etc. These changes can occur only if the substance gets some heat from outside.

 Activity 6

To demonstrate an endothermic reaction.

Materials required A bottle of perfume.

Method Spray some perfume on your hand. You will see droplets of the perfume as well as feel a cool sensation on the skin of your hand. Soon the liquid vanishes. Can you explain why?

In the activity above the perfume droplets get heat from the body through the skin and change to vapour (dry up). The skin feels cool because it loses heat to the perfume droplets. The drying up (or vaporization) of the perfume is an endothermic reaction.

 **Recall**

- Interaction between substances is essential for a change to occur.
- Energy change is a prominent feature of any type of change.
- Heat is absorbed in an endothermic reaction.
- Heat is evolved in an exothermic reaction.

EXERCISES

1. **Classify the following changes as physical or chemical**
   - (a) freezing of ice
   - (b) boiling of an egg
   - (c) grinding of wheat
   - (d) glowing of an electric lamp
   - (e) rusting of iron
   - (f) rolling of dough into a chapati
   - (g) photosynthesis in green plants
   - (h) cutting of carrot into pieces
   - (i) making toffee from butter and sugar
   - (j) breaking of a glass tumbler

2. **Fill in the blanks**
   - (a) New substances are formed in a _____.
   - (b) Energy changes are involved in a _____.
   - (c) Absorption of heat occurs in a _____ change.
   - (d) Glowing of an electric lamp gives _____ and _____.
   - (e) Melting of wax is a _____ change.
   - (f) Changes like earthquakes, floods in rivers, etc., are _____ to man.
   - (g) Oscillatory motion of the feet of the tailor to make the wheel rotate is a _____ change.
   - (h) Burning of a candle is a _____ change.

3. **Match the following**

Column A	Column B
(i) Condensation, evaporation and boiling	(a) Undesirable changes
(ii) Preservation of milk	(b) Condensation
(iii) Chemical change	(c) Physical changes
(iv) Hurricane, earthquake	(d) Pasteurization
(v) Changes that occur at regular intervals	(e) New substance
(vi) Usually, chemical changes involve	(f) Desirable change
(vii) Evolution of heat on addition of sodium hydroxide flakes to water	(g) Non-periodic change
	(h) Periodic change
	(i) Energy change
	(j) Chemical change
	(k) Endothermic reaction
	(l) Exothermic reaction

4. Fill in *Yes* or *No* or write the answer to the questions in Table 5.2

Table 5.2

	Heating of ammonium chloride	Burning of petrol or diesel in the engine of a car	Dissolution of sugar in water
Is the change physical or chemical?			
Is the energy absorbed or given out?			
Formation of a new substance			
Can the starting substance be recovered?			
Are the properties of the new substance same?			

5. Identify the type of change and state whether energy is absorbed or given out in each one of the following:
   (a) setting off of a firework
   (b) glowing of an electric lamp
   (c) cooking of food
   (d) volcanic eruption
   (e) dissoution of ammonium chloride in water

6. State the type of change represented by the following processes. Give reasons for your answer:
   (a) Painting a piece of wood
   (b) Burning of coal
   (c) Withering of leaves
   (d) Stretching of a rubber band

7. In a pressure-kerosene stove, we pump kerosene and convert it into kerosene vapours and then light it. The vapours catch fire.
   (a) Identify the physical and chemical change involved in the process. (b) Tabulate the differences between physical changes and chemical changes.

THINK AND ANSWER

1. What kind of a change is represented by the freezing of lakes and ponds in cold countries?

2. Figure 5.9 represents the combustion chamber of a rocket, where the fuel is burnt to release hot gases.

(a) What will happen to the rocket on release of the hot expanding gases?

(b) What kind of a change occurs in the combustion chamber? Give reasons for your answer.

(c) Name the substance that is required to burn the fuel.

(d) Classify the above change in as many ways as you can.

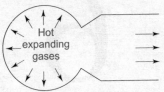

Fig. 5.9 Combustion chamber of a rocket

 ## Teacher's Notes

- The teacher can introduce the idea of change by performing simple acts — drinking water, writing and rubbing on the blackboard, making children stand in a queue according to their height, length of hair, etc.

- Students could be educated on the undesirable changes occurring within the school and outside. The teacher can encourage the students to have a constructive plan to prevent the following undesirable practices:

    (a) In school—dumping of waste matter, newspapers, etc., in the classrooms and corridors, wastage of electricity and water, use of plastic bags.

    (b) Outside—Wastage of drinking water, dumping of household and industrial waste, over-consumption of fuel, increase in habitation leading to deforestation.

6

- Importance of measurement
- Units
- Standard units
- Fundamental and derived units
- SI system of units
- Measurement of length, mass, time, temperature, area, volume

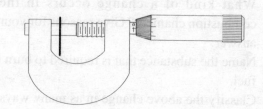

Measurement

A shopkeeper in a cloth shop measures out 5 *metres* of cloth using a steel scale. A fruit vendor measures out 1 *kilogram* of mangoes by using weighing scales. You use your wrist watch to measure the time you have taken to walk back from school, which is 30 *minutes*.

Ramu is sick. The doctor uses a thermometer to measure his temperature which is 38 degrees celsius.

These examples illustrate how measurement plays a vital role in our lives. In fact, it is the basis of all scientific study and experimentation. It can be said that measurement is used to determine an unknown quantity by comparing it with a known quantity. We see that each of the examples of measurements considered above involved the following:

 (i) a unit for the physical quantity (length, mass, time, temperature, etc.)—metres, kilogram, minutes, degrees celsius, etc.
 (ii) a number that tells us how many times the unit is contained in the physical quantity being measured—5, 1, 30, 38, etc.
(iii) a measuring instrument—steel scale, weighing scales, wristwatch, thermometer, etc.

UNITS

We have seen that the measurement of each physical quantity requires the use of a unit.

Let us take an example. Suppose you are measuring the height of your father. If you say that his height is 155 centimetres, you can get an idea of how tall he is. But, if you say that his height is just 155, without specifying the unit, you get no idea of how tall he is; he could be 155 metres or 155 kilometres tall!

Thus, a unit is an essential part of every measurement. In the olden days, people often used to devise their own convenient units for measurement. For instance, to measure length, people used cubits. One cubit was the length of an arm from the elbow to the tip of the middle finger (Fig. 6.1). Similarly, another unit used was the handspan (Fig. 6.2).

Try measuring the length of a table using a cubit or a handspan and compare it with the results of some of your friends. You may find that some of your friends get results which are different from yours. Why do you think this happens?

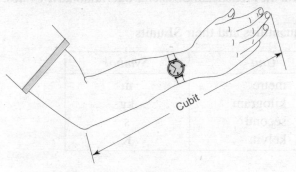

Fig. 6.1   A cubit

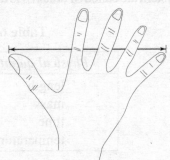

Fig. 6.2   A handspan

If everyone has to get the same answer on measuring the same object, then they need to use units of the same measure.

A unit which always has the same measure for every person is called a standard unit.

STANDARD UNITS—FUNDAMENTAL AND DERIVED UNITS

Some of the physical quantities that we commonly measure are length, mass and time. Let us see what these quantities mean and what their standard units are.

Length is the measure of the distance between two points.

The standard unit for measurement of length is a *metre*, abbreviated as m.

Mass of a body is the quantity of matter contained in it.

The standard unit for measurement of mass is a *kilogram*, abbreviated as kg.

Time is the measure of the moments that pass during the occurrence of any event.

The standard unit for measurement of time is *second*, abbreviated as s.

These three units—m, kg and s are known as the *fundamental units* and make up the *MKS system* of units. Units of other physical quantities such as area, volume, speed, etc., are obtained as some combination of these fundamental units. Such units are called *derived units*.

THE SI SYSTEM OF UNITS

Scientists, the world over, have adopted a set of standard units for measurement. This set of standard units is known as the *International System of Units* and the units in this system are called SI units. SI is the abbreviation for the French name *Système International d'Unités*.

Table 6.1   Physical quantities and their SI units

Physical quantity	Unit	Symbol
length	metre	m
mass	kilogram	kg
time	second	s
temperature	kelvin	K

However, the commonly used unit for temperature is degree celsius (°C).

In India, the national standards for all SI units are maintained by the National Physical Laboratory (NPL), New Delhi. A prototype (sample) of the standard metre and standard kilogram are kept at NPL. The metre rods and kilogram weights commonly used are copies of these standard measures. The standard of time is also maintained at NPL. The pip... pip ... sound that you hear before some news bulletins on All India Radio may be used to set your watches or clocks to the correct time. These time signals are provided by NPL with the help of an atomic (caesium) clock.

Correct Method of Writing Units and Their Symbols

The following should be kept in mind, when units or their symbols are needed:
1. Symbols for SI units are written with a small letter, e.g., kg, m, s. Only for litre, we use the symbol ℓ.
2. Symbols for units that are named after a scientist are written with a capital letter, e.g., K (kelvin), °C(celsius), N (newton), J (joule), etc.
3. Symbols for units are not followed by a full stop, unless they occur at the end of a sentence, e.g., m and not m., kg and not kg., etc.
4. Symbols of units remain unaltered in the plural, i.e., you would write 100 m and not 100 ms.

5. The name of a unit written in full is always written with a small letter including those units that are named after scientists, e.g., kelvin, ampere, newton, etc.

The SI system of units has the following advantages over the older systems of units:
1. They use a decimal system, i.e., multiples of ten, so they are more convenient.
2. They are easily reproducible and do not change with time.

Recall

- A unit which always has the same measure for every person is called a standard unit.
- The units m, kg and s are called fundamental units while other units are called derived units.
- Units must be written using the correct method.
- The internationally accepted system of units is the S.I. system.
- It is often convenient to use multiples and submultiples of units.

Let's Answer

1. What units would you use for measuring the lengths of each of the following?
   (i) The length of your bedroom.
   (ii) The thickness of your finger.
   (iii) The distance between Delhi and Madras.
   (iv) The thickness of a piece of wire.
   (v) The length of your pen.
   (vi) The diameter of a piece of chalk.
   (vii) The height of your school building.
   (viii) The distance between your home and the nearest market.
   (ix) The length of a grasshopper.
   (x) Your height.

2. Point out the mistakes in the following:
   (i) 100 Newton
   (ii) 20 mg
   (iii) 350 j
   (iv) 100 Kg of wheat

3. Complete the following:
   (i) 5 m 40 cm = _____ cm
   (ii) 4 km 75 m = _____ m
   (iii) 9007 m = _____ km _____ m
   (iv) 573 m = _____ m _____ cm
   (v) 25004 m = _____ km _____ m
   (vi) 3 cm 6 mm = _____ mm
   (vii) 5463 cm = _____ m _____ cm
   (viii) 901 mm = _____ cm _____ mm
   (ix) 9000 m = _____ km _____ m
   (x) 403 cm = _____ m _____ cm

Multiples and Submultiples of Fundamental Units

A metre is roughly the distance from one shoulder to the tip of the middle finger on the opposite arm of a grown up person. It is a convenient unit for measuring the length of a cloth, a table, a room, etc. But if you want to measure the length of your pencil or note-book, then you will need a smaller unit. For this we may use a centimetre, abbreviated as cm, which is one-hundredth of a metre. Even this may be too large to measure the thickness of a coin. For this we may use an even smaller unit, a millimetre, abbreviated as mm, which is one-tenth of a centimetre.

On the other hand, if you had to measure very large distances such as the distance between two towns or the distance from home to school, you would need a unit larger than the metre. For this you may use a kilometre, abbreviated as km, which is equal to a thousand metres.

Table 6.2   Prefixes—Abbreviations and Meanings

Prefix	Meaning	Abbreviation
kilo	thousand times (1000)	k
centi	one-hundredth $\left(\dfrac{1}{100}\right)$	c
milli	one-thousandth $\left(\dfrac{1}{1000}\right)$	m

$$1 \text{ km} = 1000 \text{ m} \qquad\qquad 1 \text{ m} = 1/1000 \text{ km}$$
$$1 \text{ m} = 100 \text{ cm} = 1000 \text{ mm} \qquad 1 \text{ cm} = 1/100 \text{ m}$$
$$1 \text{ cm} = 10 \text{ mm} \qquad\qquad 1 \text{ mm} = 1/1000 \text{ m} = 1/10 \text{ cm}$$

Similarly, we use multiples and submultiples of the units of mass, i.e., kilogram (kg) for the measurement of the masses of different quantities. For measuring rice, pulses, sugar, etc., at the grocer's, you may use kilogram as the unit, but if you want to measure the mass of a handful of spices or a roll of cotton wool, you need a smaller unit of mass. For this you may use a gram, abbreviated as g, which is one-thousandth of a kilogram. Tiny tablets or medicinal powders may be measured in still smaller units, i.e., milligram, abbreviated as mg, which is one-thousandth of a gram. For measuring the mass of huge bags of cement we may use a quintal, which is equal to one hundred kilograms. Again, for measuring the mass of a truck we may use a metric ton, which is equal to ten quintals. Thus,

1 kg	= 1000 g	10 quintals	= 1 tonne (metric ton) = 1000 kg
1 g	= 1000 mg	1g	= 1/1000 kg
1 quintal	= 100 kg	1 mg	= 1/1000 g

You have studied that the standard unit for measurement of time is a second. Smaller intervals of time may be measured in milliseconds, abbreviated as ms, which is one-thousandth of a second. Larger units of time are a minute, abbreviated as min, which is equal to sixty seconds, and an hour, abbreviated as h, which is equal to sixty minutes, a day which is equal to 24 hours, a year which is equal to 365 days, etc.

Recall

- Multiples and submultiples are required because sometimes we may need to measure quantities that are much smaller or much greater than the standard.
- The standard for distance is a metre and its multiple is a kilometre and its submultiples centimetre and millimetre.
- The standard for weight is gram and its multiples are tonnes, quintals and kilograms, while its submultiple is a milligram.
- The standard for time is a second. A millisecond is one-thousandth of a second, while a minute is equal to sixty seconds and an hour equal to 60 minutes.

Let's Answer

1. Match the mass in Column A with the unit to be used as given in Column B:

Column A	Column B
a railway engine	quintal
a small packet of chilli powder	kg
a sack of wheat	mg
huge bags of sand	g
an aspirin tablet	metric tonne

2. Fill in the blanks:
   (i) 7650 kg = _____ g
   (ii) 3050 mg = _____ g _____ mg
   (iii) 45 kg = _____ g = _____ mg
   (iv) 250 g = _____ kg = _____ mg
   (v) 3500 kg = _____ quintal
   (vi) 45 tonne = _____ quintal = _____ kg

3. Complete the following:
   (i) 250 milliseconds (ms) = _____ s
   (ii) 45 s = _____ minute (min) = _____ h
   (iii) 20 min = _____ s
   (iv) 4 hours (h) = 4 × 60 min = _____ s
   (v) 3 min 15 s = _____ s
   (vi) 2 hr 10 min = _____ min
   (vii) 5 days = _____ hour = _____ min

MEASUREMENT OF LENGTH

The commonest instrument one uses to measure length is the foot ruler.

Activity 1

To measure any straight line in a simple manner using the commonest instrument.

Materials required   Ruler, paper, pencil.

Method   Place the ruler on the sheet of paper as shown in Figure 6.3. Your eye must be exactly above the ruler, otherwise you will get an inaccurate reading. Note the reading at point A and B. At point A the reading is 3.0 cm, while at point B the reading is 6.0 cm. Hence the length of the straight line is 3.0 cm.

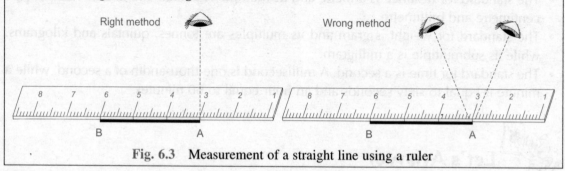

Fig. 6.3   Measurement of a straight line using a ruler

If the ruler is broken or worn out near its zero mark, do not use the zero mark, but use any other full mark on the ruler, say 1.0 cm, and subtract the reading of this mark from the reading at the other end.

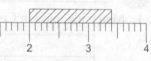

Fig. 6.4

To measure very small lengths such as the diameter of a fine wire or fine machine parts, scientists use instruments such as vernier callipers or the micrometer screw gauge (Figs. 6.5 and 6.6). Microscopes are also used to measure very small lengths such as the sizes of micro-organisms (Fig. 6.7).

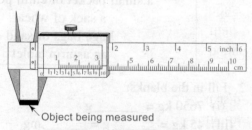

Object being measured

Fig. 6.5   Vernier callipers

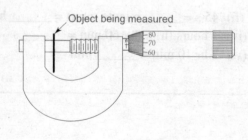

Object being measured

Fig. 6.6   Screw gauge

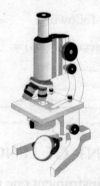

Fig. 6.7   Microscope

MEASUREMENT OF MASS

Mass of an object is usually measured by means of a balance. A most common balance is the beam balance. It consists of a horizontal beam supported in the centre and two similar pans suspended at equal distances from the centre of the beam (Fig. 6.8). The object, whose mass is to be determined, is placed in one of the pans and standard weights are placed in the other pan and adjusted, till the beam is perfectly horizontal. The total of these weights gives the mass of the object.

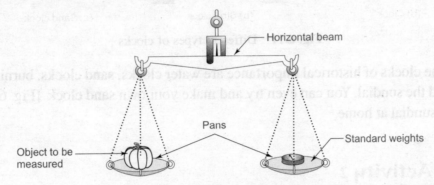

Fig. 6.8   Beam balance

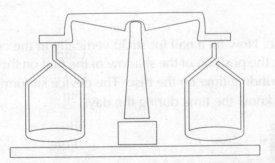

Fig. 6.9   Physical (laboratory) balance

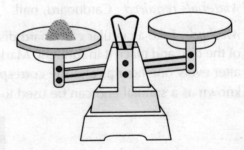

Fig. 6.10   Commercial balance

MEASUREMENT OF TIME

The common time-measuring devices used nowadays are clocks and watches. Electronic or digital display clocks and watches are also increasingly being used. For measuring very small intervals of time in the laboratory or in sports, we use stop clocks and stop watches which can measure accurately upto one-tenth or even one-hundredth of a second [Fig. 6.11(a) and (b)].

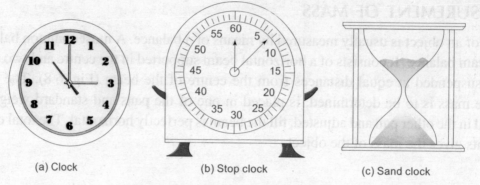

(a) Clock   (b) Stop clock   (c) Sand clock

Fig. 6.11   Different types of clocks

Some of the clocks of historical importance are water clocks, sand clocks, burning candle clocks, and the sundial. You can even try and make your own sand clock [Fig. 6.11(c)] or your own sundial at home.

Activity 2

To make your own sundial.

Materials required   Cardboard, nail.

Method   Take a circular cardboard disc. Now fix a nail (or stick) vertically in the centre of the disc and place it in sunlight. Mark the position of the shadow of the nail on the disc after every one hour as also the corresponding time on the disc. The device so formed is known as a sundial and can be used to know the time during the day.

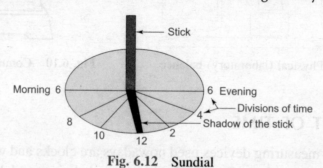

Fig. 6.12   Sundial

MEASUREMENT OF TEMPERATURE

Another commonly measured physical quantity is *temperature* which *is the degree of hotness or coldness of a body.*

The device used for measuring temperature is called a *thermometer*.

Figure 6.13 shows you a thermometer. Most of you must have used a thermometer when you have fever. Thermometers are usually made of glass and consist of a long part called the stem on which degrees celsius are marked. At the lower end of the stem is the bulb which contains a shiny liquid called *mercury*. Inside the stem is a very thin inner tube called the *capillary tube*. When the bulb of the thermometer is placed in hot water, the mercury rises up in the capillary tube and the mark upto which it rises gives the temperature in degrees celsius (°C).

Mercury is easily seen in the capillary tube because of its shiny colour. Mercury being a liquid metal, heats up easily and so the thermometer can show even quick changes in temperature.

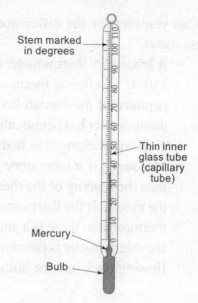

Stem marked in degrees

Thin inner glass tube (capillary tube)

Mercury

Bulb

Fig. 6.13   A thermometer

In the SI system temperatures are measured in kelvin. In the kelvin scale the melting point of ice is 273 K, while the boiling point of water is 373 K, with 100 divisions between them. What is the body temperature of a healthy person in kelvin? It is 273 + 37 = 310 K.

Different thermometers are used for measuring different ranges of temperature. Carefully look at the thermometer that the doctor uses to measure the temperature of your body when you are sick. What are the highest and lowest temperatures that this thermometer can measure?

For measuring the temperature of the human body, doctors normally use a special kind of thermometer called a *clinical thermometer*. Figure 6.14 shows the diagrams of a clinical thermometer and a laboratory thermometer.

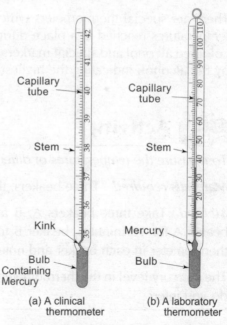

Capillary tube

Stem

Kink

Bulb Containing Mercury

Capillary tube

Stem

Mercury

Bulb

(a) A clinical thermometer

(b) A laboratory thermometer

Fig. 6.14   Types of thermometers

Can you identify the difference between a clinical thermometer and a laboratory thermometer?

- A laboratory thermometer can be used to measure any temperature between 0 °C and 110 °C. A clinical thermometer is used to measure only small changes in the temperature of the human body (normal is 37 °C). Therefore, the stem of the clinical thermometer has demarcations from 35 °C to 42 °C only, to enable the doctor to detect even small changes in body temperature.
- Moreover, if a laboratory thermometer is used to measure a person's temperature, then the reading of the thermometer has to be taken while the thermometer is still in the mouth. If the thermometer is taken out, its reading will change. But in the clinical thermometer, there is a small bend or *kink* at the bottom of the capillary tube. When the thermometer is taken out of the patient's mouth, this kink stops the mercury from flowing back into the bulb and the temperature can be comfortably read.

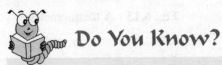 **Do You Know?**

Maximum and Minimum thermometer

There are special thermometers which are used to record the maximum and minimum temperatures reached at a place during a given period of time. These thermometers use coloured alcohol and special markers which record the highest and lowest levels reached by the alcohol, indicating the highest and lowest temperatures experienced.

 **Activity 3**

To measure the temperatures of different samples using a thermometer.

Materials required Three beakers, three thermometers, bunsen burner, water, clock.

Method Take three beakers A, B and C containing the same amount of water. Heat beaker A for 10 minutes, beaker B for 5 minutes and beaker C for 15 minutes. Insert a thermometer in each beaker and note the level to which the mercury rises.

The mercury level in the thermometer is highest in beaker C and lowest in beaker B. What do you infer?

From the above activity we can infer that water in beaker C was the hottest of all.

Figure 6.15 shows some of the common temperatures that we come across. The temperature at which water freezes is 0 °C, while the temperature at which water boils and changes to steam is 100 °C. The normal body temperature of a healthy person is 37 °C.

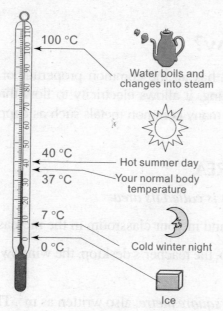

100 °C — Water boils and changes into steam

40 °C — Hot summer day

37 °C — Your normal body temperature

7 °C — Cold winter night

0 °C — Ice

Fig. 6.15   Some common temperatures

Recall

- Length is measured using a ruler or other suitable devices.
- Mass is usually measured using a beam balance.
- Time is measured with the help of clocks or watches.
- The degree of hotness or coldness of a body is called its temperature.
- Temperature is measured using a thermometer in units of degree celsius (°C).
- Mercury is the liquid commonly used in a thermometer.
- A laboratory thermometer can be used to measure temperatures between 0 °C and 110 °C.
- A clinical thermometer is used to measure small changes in body temperature and is marked with temperatures from 35 °C to 42 °C only.

Let's Answer

1. What are vernier callipers and the screw gauge used for?
2. What instrument is used to time a 200 m race?
3. What is (i) the melting point of ice (ii) the boiling point of water (iii) body temperature of a healthy person?
4. Why can't you use a laboratory thermometer to measure the body temperature of a person?

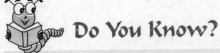 **Do You Know?**

Mercury is a liquid metal. It has all the common properties of metals, for example, it increases in volume on heating, it allows electricity to flow through it, it is shiny, etc. Mercury is also heavier than many common metals such as copper, aluminium, etc.

MEASUREMENT OF AREA

The total surface of an object is called its area.

List the following objects found in your classroom in the increasing order of their areas:

The blackboard, your desktop, the teacher's desktop, the window pane, the ceiling, the top of the duster.

The standard unit of area is a *square metre*, also written as m^2. This is the area of a square surface, each side of which is of length 1 m. Multiple and submultiple units of area are:
  (i) square cm (cm^2)—the area of a square, each side of which is of length 1 cm.
  (ii) square km (km^2)—the area of a square, each side of which is of length 1 km.

Table 6.3 gives the relationship between different units of area.

Table 6.3   Different units of area

$$1 \ cm^2 = 10 \ mm \times 10 \ mm$$
$$= 100 \ mm^2$$
$$1 \ m^2 = 100 \ cm \times 100 \ cm$$
$$= 10000 \ cm^2$$
$$1 \ hectare = 100 \ m \times 100 \ m = 10000 \ m^2$$
$$1 \ km^2 = 1000 \ m \times 1000 \ m$$
$$= 1000000 \ m^2$$

Area of a Regular Surface

You have learnt in mathematics that:

Area of a square = side × side

Area of a rectangle = length × breadth

Area of other regular figures may be calculated using formulae that you will learn in higher classes.

MEASUREMENT OF VOLUME

The space occupied by a body is called its volume.

The standard unit of volume is a *cubic metre*, also written as m³. This is the volume of a cube, each side of which is of length 1 m.

A submultiple of this is a cubic centimetre, also written as cm³. This is the volume of a cube in which the length of each of its sides is 1 cm.

Volume of Liquids

Volumes of liquids are usually measured in a unit called a *litre*, abbreviated as ℓ. A submultiple of a litre is a millilitre, also written as mℓ.

$$1\,\ell = 1000\text{ m}\ell;\ 1\text{ m}\ell = 1\text{ cm}^3$$

For measuring the volume of a liquid, various kinds of measuring vessels are used, some of which are shown in Figure 6.16.

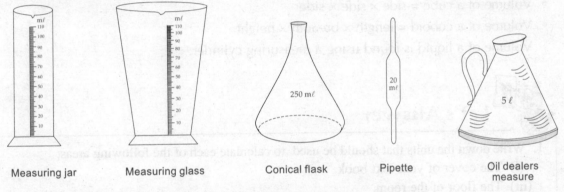

| Measuring jar | Measuring glass | Conical flask | Pipette | Oil dealers measure |

Fig. 6.16   Various kinds of measuring vessels

 ## Activity 4

To measure the volume of water contained in a glass tumbler.

Materials required   A glass tumbler, measuring jar, water.

Method   Take a glass tumbler and pour some water into it. Take a measuring jar. This is usually marked in mℓ. Gently pour the water from the tumbler into the measuring jar. Read the level of the water in the measuring jar, keeping the eye exactly at water level. This reading gives the volume of water in the tumbler in mℓ (Fig. 6.17).

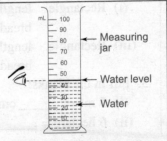

Fig. 6.17   Measuring the volume of water

Volume of Regular Solids

The volumes of regular solids such as a cube or a cuboid are given by the following formulae:

Volume of a cube = side × side × side

Volume of a cuboid = length × breadth × height

Thus, $1 \text{ m}^3 = 1 \text{ m} \times 1 \text{ m} \times 1 \text{ m} = 100 \text{ cm} \times 100 \text{ cm} \times 100 \text{ cm} = 1000000 \text{ cm}^3$

 Recall

- The total surface of an object is called its area. Area is measured in units of m^2, cm^2, km^2, hectare, etc.
- Area of a square = side × side
- Area of a rectangle = length × breadth
- Volume of the body is the space occupied by it. It is measured in units of m^3, cm^3.
- Volume of a liquid is measured in litre (ℓ) or millilitre (mℓ)
- Volume of a cube = side × side × side
- Volume of a cuboid = length × breadth × height
- Volume of a liquid is found using a measuring cylinder.

 Let's Answer

1. Write down the units that should be used to calculate each of the following areas:
   (i) The cover of your text book.
   (iii) The floor of the room.
   (iv) The area of the school playground.
   (v) The total area of Delhi.

2. Calculate the area of the following figures:
   (i) Rectangle: length = 6 m
                  breadth = 5 m
   (ii) Square: side length = 8 cm
   (iii) Rectangle: length = 9 cm
                  breadth = 4 cm
   (iv) Square: side length = 7 m

3. Fill in the blanks:
   (i) $5 \text{ m}^2 = $ _____ cm^2
   (iii) $45 \text{ cm}^2 = $ _____ mm^2
   (ii) 6 hectare = _____ m^2
   (iv) $3 \text{ km}^2 = $ _____ m^2

(Contd...)

4. A rectangular block has length 12 cm, breadth 5 cm and height 7 cm. Find its volume in cubic centimetres.
5. What units would you use to measure the following volumes?
   (i) Volume of liquid in a squash bottle.
   (ii) Volume of your room.
   (iii) Volume of an ice cube.
   (iv) Volume of the inside of a bus.
6. Find the volume of a cube, each side of which is 5 m. Express your answer in m^3 and cm^3.

Department of Weights and Measures

The government of India passes laws to ensure that

- uniform units of measurement are used throughout the country
- accurate measuring instruments are used
- correct standards of measurements (e.g. weights) are used.

All standard weights and measures as well as measuring instruments are required to be periodically checked and certified by the Department of Weights and Measures, Government of India.

EXERCISES

1. **Mark the following sentences as *True* or *False***
   (a) 1/4 kg is equal to 250 g.
   (b) 1 m^3 is equal to 1 ℓ.
   (c) The area of a field may be measured in hectares.
   (d) The mass of a cake of toilet soap would be measured in quintals.
   (e) A clinical thermometer measures temperature from 50 °C to 100 °C.

2. **Fill in the blanks**
   (a) The three fundamental units are _____, _____,_____.
   (b) One gram is _____ of a kg.
   (c) Area of an irregular surface is measured by a _____.
   (d) The volume of a cube is given by _____.
   (e) One hectare is _____ m^2.

3. **Answer the following questions briefly**
   (i) Write ·down the standard units of (a) length (b) mass (c) time (d) temperature (e) area (f) volume of a solid.
   (ii) What unit of length will be used to express:
      (a) the distance from Delhi to Shimla?

(b) the length of your trousers/skirt?

(c) the length of the palm of your hand?

(d) the thickness of a medicine tablet?

(iii) What is the mass of a body? Describe how you will make your own beam balance.

(iv) What unit of mass would you use to measure the following:

(a) your pen   (b) a bag of flour

(c) a handful of pins   (d) a baby

(e) a bunch of bananas   (f) a truck

(v) Draw a neat, labelled diagram of a laboratory thermometer and mark on it the boiling point of water, the melting point of ice and the normal human body temperature.

(vi) A water tank is of length 5 m, breadth 3 m and depth 2 m. What is the volume of the maximum amount of water it can hold? Give your answer in cubic metres, in litres and in millimetres.

(vii) Why do we need standard units for measurement?

(viii) Give two reasons as to why mercury is commonly used in a thermometer?

THINK AND ANSWER

1. Mother bought 5 packets, each containing 20 biscuits. The total mass of the biscuits was 3 kg 500 g. What was the mass of each biscuit?   (Ans. 35 g)

2. A shopkeeper has standard weights of 5 kg, 2 kg and 1 kg. A customer wants to buy 3.5 kg of rice. How will the shopkeeper manage to give the customer what he wants?

3. Five identical bottles, each of capacity 300 mℓ, are filled with water. They are then emptied into a bucket that can hold a maximum of 4 ℓ. How much more water is needed to fill up the bucket?   (Ans. 2.5 ℓ)

4. A floor has a length of 4 m and a breadth of 3 m. It is to be covered with square tiles of side 20 cm. How many tiles will be needed to completely cover the floor?   (Ans. 300 tiles)

5. You are given a glass filled with milk. How will you measure out exactly half of its volume without using any measuring vessel?   [*Hint:* Use another identical empty glass]

6. 1 cm^3 volume is equal to 1 mℓ. Now calculate how many litres are there in 1 m^3.
                                                                                        (Ans. 1000)

 Teacher's Notes

- Classroom demonstration of common measuring instruments, or a visit to the laboratory to see how these are used, would greatly help in making students familiar with measurement methods.
- Some activities using hands-on measurements by students would help them understand and appreciate measurements better.
- A visit to NPL where they would be able to see the prototypes of the standard metre, kilogram, second, etc., would enrich the students ideas on standard units.

7

- The living and the non-living world
- Classification of living things
- Plant kingdom
- Animal kingdom
- Variety in living organisms— shape and size, food, habitat, habit
- Characteristics of living things
- Naming of living organisms
- Importance of plants and animals

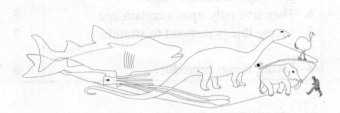

Living Organisms
Characteristics and Classification

THE LIVING AND THE NON-LIVING WORLD

We are surrounded by many objects. We find that some of these objects can move, respire, eat food, etc. These are called living things. For example, animals and plants. *The study of living things is called biology.* All the other objects which do not perform any such activities as moving, breathing, etc., are called non-living things. For example, rocks, soil, water, cars, etc. Let us see the major differences between the living and the non-living (Table 7.1).

Table 7.1 Differences between the living and the non-living

Living things	Non-living things
1. Living things are made up of small units called cells.	1. Non-living things have no cells.
2. They respire.	2. They do not respire.
3. Living things need nutrition to carry on their daily activities.	3. Non-living things do not need any nutrition. If they have to perform some work, they need fuel.
4. They excrete materials that are harmful to their body.	4. They do not possess any system for excretion.

(Contd.)

Table 7.1   (Contd.)

Living things	Non-living things
5. Living things grow—plants grow throughout their life and animals grow upto a certain stage.	5. Non-living things do not show any kind of growth patterns.
6. They live only upto a certain age.	6. They have no definite lifespan.
7. Living things respond to stimuli.	7. Non-living things do not respond to stimuli.
8. Living things reproduce.	8. Non-living things do not reproduce.

CLASSIFICATION OF LIVING THINGS

The living world can be divided into the *plant kingdom* and the *animal kingdom*.

The plant kingdom can be classified into flowering plants and non-flowering plants (Fig. 7.1).

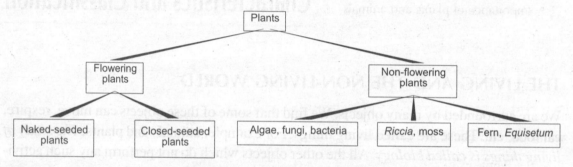

Fig. 7.1   Classification of plants

Flowering Plants

These are the plants which produce flowers, e.g., guava, mango, *Cycas*, etc. Flowering plants can be further divided into:

Naked-seeded Plants   The seeds of these plants have no cover over them and so are called naked, e.g., *Cycas* [Fig. 7.2(a)], *Pinus*, etc.

Closed-seeded Plants   The seeds of these plants are enclosed in a fruit, e.g., mango, plum, guava, sunflower, etc. [Fig. 7.2 (b)].

(a) *Cycas*—A plant producing naked
    seeds without fruits

(b) Sunflower—A flowering plant
    with enclosed seeds

Fig. 7.2 Examples of flowering plants

Non-flowering Plants

These plants do not bear flowers, e.g., bacteria, fungi, etc. (Fig. 7.3). They are of the following five types:

Algae   These are green plants found in rivers, ponds, sewers, and ditches. They float in water and most of them are visible to the naked eye, e.g., *Spirogyra*.

Fungi   They grow on dead vegetable matter and appear white and hairy, e.g., mushrooms.

Bacteria   These occur almost anywhere — water, air, soil, food stuffs, fruits, and vegetables. Many float in air.

Algae, Fungi and Bacteria have no leaves, stems or roots.

Riccia and Moss   It is a green plant which grows like a carpet on wet ground and damp walls. *Moss* also grows on damp walls.

Both riccia and moss have a plant body which is not differentiated into stem and root.

Ferns   They grow in cool, shady places. Ferns are found both on hills and in plains.

The plant body of ferns is differentiated into root, stem and leaves.

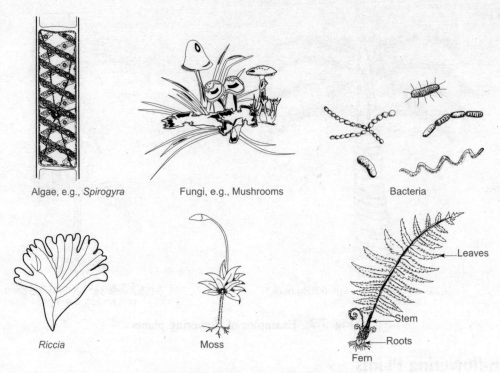

Fig. 7.3   Non-flowering plants

Classification of Flowering Plants

Flowering plants can also be classified on the basis of their shape and size, lifespan and habitat.

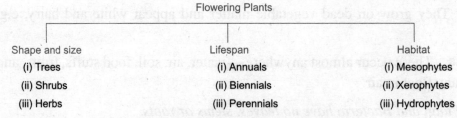

Fig. 7.4   Classification of flowering plants

Based on Shape and Size

There are three types of flowering plants based on shape and size, namely,

Trees

1. They are tall and large plants.
2. They have one main stem—the trunk.
3. The trunk may produce branches, twigs and leaves. However, coconut and palm trees do not produce branches.

4. They live for a long period
   Examples: Mango, banyan.

Shrubs

1. They are medium-sized plants.
2. They also have a woody and profusely branched stem.
3. All branches arise from the early part of the stem.
4. They do not grow tall.
5. They can live for many years.
   Examples: *Bougainvillea*, henna, *Lantana*, lemon.

Herbs

1. They are small plants with soft and delicate stems.
2. They do not grow tall. The maximum height of these plants is 1 m.
3. They live for a short period (for one or two seasons).
   Examples: Sunflower, mustard, wheat, paddy.

Based on Lifespan

Based on lifespan they are of the following three types:

Annuals   A plant whose life cycle, from germination of the seed to appearance of fruits, is completed in one season. For example, wheat, paddy, mustard, *Petunia*, cereals are all annuals.

Biennials   A plant whose life cycle needs two seasons. They grow the vegetative parts (leaf and stem) during the first season and in the second season they produce flowers and fruits. For example, plants such as raddish, carrot, turnip and potato need two years to complete their life cycles.

Perennials   Are plants which live for more than two years. For example, Bamboo, mango, palm, neem, babool, etc.

Based on Habitat

Flowering plants, based on habitat, are of the following three types:

Mesophytes   They grow on land and need only a moderate amount of water supply for their survival. Examples: Mango, banyan, etc.

Xerophytes   (*Xero-* → desert, *-phytes* → plants). They live in dry climates and survive on a minimum amount of water. They have long roots and bear thin and spiny leaves to reduce evaporation. Examples: Cactus, *Acacia*, etc.

Hydrophytes   (*Hydro-* → water, *-phytes* → plants). These plants grow in water. The roots of such plants are poorly developed or even absent. Examples: Lotus, water chestnut, water lily, etc.

Recall

- Living things are entirely different from non-living things.
- The living world is classified into the plant kingdom and the animal kingdom.
- Plants can be flowering or non-flowering.
- Depending on shape and size, lifespan and habitat plants can be categorized into various groups.

Let's Answer

1. State any three differences between the living and the non-living world.
2. Mention the names of two non-flowering plants and their uses.
3. On what basis are plants categorized as trees, shrubs and herbs?
4. What do you understand by biennial plants?
5. What are the characteristics of xerophytes?

ANIMAL KINGDOM

The animal kingdom has been divided into two major sub-kingdoms, vertebrates and invertebrates (Fig. 7.5).

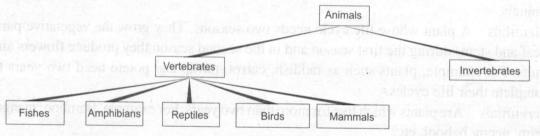

Fig. 7.5   Classification of animals

Vertebrates

These are the animals with a *backbone*. Their bodies have a distinct head, trunk and tail, e.g., fish, frog, snake, crow, horse, rat, human being, etc. (Fig. 7.6). Vertebrates can be divided into five distinct groups as follows:

Fishes   They live in water and have a streamlined body which enables them to swim easily. Fishes have a body skeleton which is either made up of bones or of cartilages, e.g., mackerel, *Rohu*, sardine, shark, etc.

Amphibians   These animals live both on land and in water. Amphibians lay eggs in water. These eggs hatch into tadpoles which can swim using their tails. The tadpole develops into the adult, e.g., frog, toad, salamander.

Reptiles   They have a sleek body covered with scales. Reptiles have lungs with the help of which they breathe. They lay eggs with tough shells, e.g., snake, lizard, turtle, etc.

Birds   Birds have feathers and also a streamlined body which aids them in flying. They have a light skeletal system. In fact, their bones are hollow and have air cavities to help them to fly easily, e.g., pigeon, owl, peacock, etc.

Mammals   They generally give birth to live young ones. They take care of their young ones till they are independent and can look after themselves, e.g., horse, cow, whale, monkey, human beings, etc.

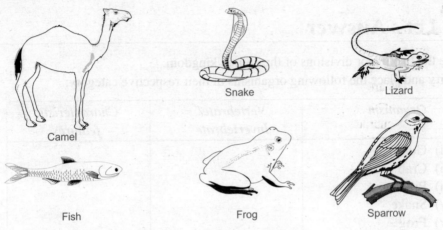

Fig. 7.6   **Some vertebrates**

Invertebrates

These are the animals without a backbone. Worms, leeches, snails, all insects, centipedes, millipedes, butterflies, etc., belong to this group. Some animals such as crabs, flies, shrimps, etc., have a tough outer skin called the *cuticle*. This gives them support (Fig. 7.7).

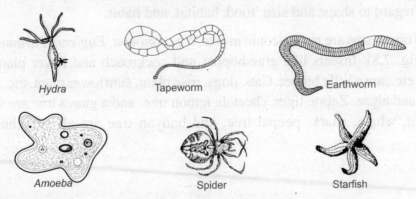

Fig. 7.7   **Some invertebrates**

Recall

- The animal kingdom is divided into vertebrate and invertebrate animals.
- Vertebrates are animals with a backbone, whereas animals without a backbone are called invertebrates.
- The vertebrates can be classified into five classes, namely, fishes, amphibians, reptiles, birds, and mammals.

Let's Answer

1. Name the two major divisions of the animal kingdom.
2. Identify and place the following organisms in their respective category:

Organism	Vertebrate/ Invertebrate	Characteristic features
(i) Goldfish		
(ii) Crab		
(iii) Pigeon		
(iv) Snake		
(v) Frog		
(vi) Monkey		

3. List any two important features for each of the major classes of vertebrates.

VARIETY IN LIVING ORGANISMS

We have identified about 7,50,000 organisms on this earth. These organisms show a great variety with regard to shape and size, food, habitat, and habit.

Size   Some organisms are microscopic in size, e.g., *Amoeba, Euglena, Paramecium*, bacteria, etc. (Fig. 7.8). Insects like grasshopper and cockroach and lower plants such as algae, moss, etc., are a little bigger. Cats, dogs, rose plant, sunflower plant, etc., are bigger than insects and algae. Zebra, tiger, cheetah, lemon tree, and a guava tree are still bigger. The elephant, whale, shark, peepal tree, and banyan tree are all very huge in size (Fig. 7.9).

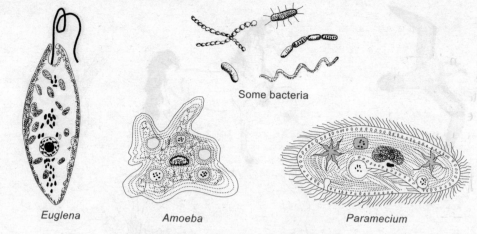

Some bacteria

Euglena   *Amoeba*   *Paramecium*

Fig. 7.8   Microscopic organisms

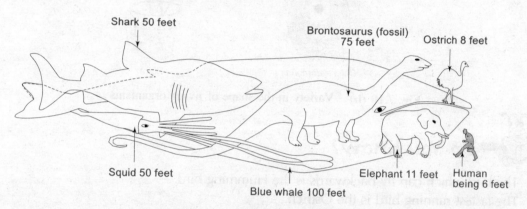

Shark 50 feet

Brontosaurus (fossil) 75 feet

Ostrich 8 feet

Squid 50 feet

Blue whale 100 feet

Elephant 11 feet

Human being 6 feet

Fig. 7.9   Animals—varying sizes

Shape   All living organisms vary from one another in their shapes. *Amoeba* has no definite shape, while *Paramecium* is slipper-shaped, fishes and birds have a streamlined body to swim in water or fly in the air. Birds have wings too, which help them to fly. Reptiles have long, sleek bodies. Land animals like the cat, dog, goat, etc., have four legs to walk. Plants generally have roots, stems and leaves. The root is found underground and the stem and leaves are above the ground. However, certain plants such as algae and fungi have no distinct roots, stems or leaves [Fig. 7.10 (a) and (b)].

Amoeba   Snake   Fish

Fig. 7.10 (a)   Variety in the shape of living organisms

107

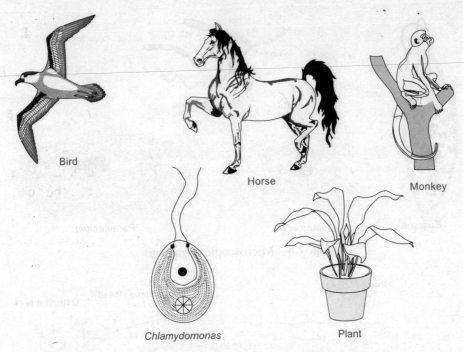

Bird

Horse

Monkey

Chlamydomonas

Plant

Fig. 7.10 (b) Variety in the shape of living organisms

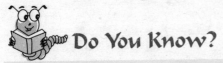

Do You Know?

- The bird which can fly backwards is the Humming bird.
- The fastest running bird is the Ostrich.
- The Golden hamster is the fastest breeding animal in the world.
- The largest land animal is the African elephant.

Food Habits

Living organisms show great variation in their food habits. They may broadly be *autotrophs* or *heterotrophs*.

Autotrophs

These are the green plants which prepare their own food with the help of chlorophyll in the presence of sunlight.

Heterotrophs

These animals cannot prepare their own food. They either eat plants or other animals. In fact, all organisms other than green plants are heterotrophs. Heterotrophs are also specific about the type of food they eat and are divided into the following five categories:

(a) **Herbivores**   These are animals which depend on plants for their food, e.g., cow, goat, elephant, giraffe, camel, zebra, etc.

(b) **Carnivores**   These are animals which kill and eat other smaller animals for their food, e.g., lion, tiger, leopard, cheetah, etc.

(c) **Omnivores**   These are animals which eat both plants and other animals, e.g., human beings.

Among the heterotrophs are also included the *parasites* and *saprophytes*.

(d) **Parasites**   These are organisms which live on other living organisms termed the *hosts*. They draw their nourishment from food already digested by the host, e.g., lice in hair, body ticks on animals and worms in our stomach (Fig. 7.11).

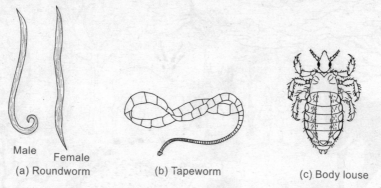

Male Female
(a) Roundworm   (b) Tapeworm   (c) Body louse

Fig. 7.11   Parasites

(e) **Saprophytes**   These are plants which cannot prepare their own food and feed on dead organic matter, e.g., fungi—mushrooms, yeast (Fig. 7.12).

(a) Mushroom   (b) Yeast

Fig. 7.12   Saprophytes

Habitat

Each living organism lives in a particular kind of place that is most suited to it.

The place in which the organism lives is called its habitat.

A habitat generally provides the organism with proper food, shelter and protection. A habitat is often shared by several organisms. For example, a dense forest is the habitat of elephants, tigers, lions, deer, snakes, ants as well as trees, shrubs, herbs, and grass (Fig. 7.13). Fishes live in ponds and lakes which are also shared by frogs, toads, snakes, water birds, water plants, insects, etc. (Fig. 7.14).

Fig. 7.13   A jungle habitat

The habitat of an animal or a plant may be on land, in water or in air. Thus, the habitats of living organisms are of four types:

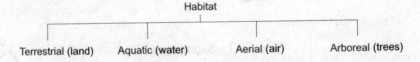

Animals and plants which live on land are *terrestrial*, e.g., humans beings, cat, dog, camel, neem tree, rose plant, etc. Animals and plants which live in water are *aquatic*, e.g., fish, lotus, water hyacinth, etc. Animals which spend much of their time in air are said to be *aerial*, e.g., birds and some insects. Animals which live on trees are said to be *arboreal*, e.g., monkeys, etc.

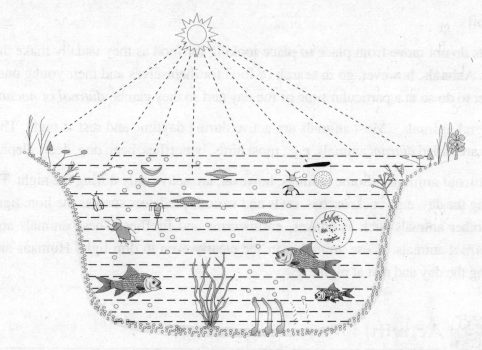

Fig. 7.14 A pond ecosystem

You will find that animals and plants living in one type of habitat often differ from those of another habitat in their features. For example, animals living in colder parts of the world have thick fur but those in the warmer parts do not. Plants of the desert have thick leaves to store water unlike the plants in other regions.

In a particular habitat, animals require homes, just like we do, to protect themselves from heat, cold, rain, and enemies, e.g., birds make nests on trees; the lion and bear live in dens; rabbits and rodents live in burrows, while ants live in holes.

Animals like the earthworm dig a deep burrow in the earth and cockroaches prefer dark corners. Bees make a big *hive* (Fig. 7.15).

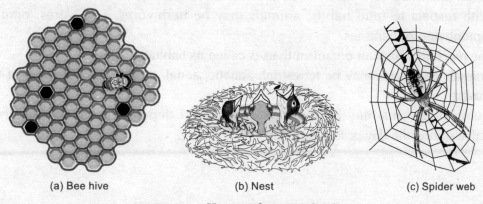

(a) Bee hive   (b) Nest   (c) Spider web

Fig. 7.15 Homes of some animals

111

Habits

Plants do not move from place to place looking for food as they usually make their own food. Animals, however, go in search of food for themselves and their young ones. They prefer to do so at a particular time of the day and so they can be *diurnal* or *nocturnal*.

Diurnal animals   Most animals are active during daytime and rest at night. These animals are called *diurnal* animals, e.g., most birds, butterflies, bear, dog, deer, elephant, etc.

Nocturnal animals   Some animals, however, are active only during the night. They rest during the day, e.g., cockroaches, owls and various predators such as the lion, tiger, wolf, and other animals such as snakes, earthworms and fireflies. These animals are called *nocturnal* animals. These animals can see clearly even in dim light. Humans are active during the day and rest at night.

Activity 1

To study the nocturnal habits of animals.

Go into your kitchen late at night and suddenly switch on the light. Observe the cockroaches that run here and there—away from the light.

If you can get an earthworm, try putting it under a table lamp. It will quickly move away from the light.

Recall

- Living organisms show variety in size, shape, habitat, food, habit, etc.
- Green plants are autotrophs, while animals are heterotrophs.
- With respect to food habits, animals may be herbivores, carnivores, omnivores, saprophytes, or parasites.
- The place in which an organism lives is called its habitat.
- Animals and plants may be terrestrial, aquatic, aerial, or arboreal with respect to their habitat.
- Living organisms may be diurnal or nocturnal depending on whether they are active during the day or in the night.

Let's Answer

1. Classify the animals given below on the basis of their habitats:

crocodile	fish	eagle
elephant	dog	cat
tortoise	duck	frog
giraffe	shark	penguin

2. Differentiate between the following:
   (i) Autotrophs and heterotrophs   (ii) Herbivores and omnivores
   (iii) Nocturnal and diurnal animals
3. What are parasites? Give examples.
4. Name a plant which is a saprophyte.
5. All saprophytes are heterotrophs. Justify the statement.

CHARACTERISTICS OF LIVING THINGS

If you observe living organisms carefully, you will find that they have some common characteristics. Now, let us make a list of these characteristics.

Living things are made up of cells

The cell is the basic unit of life. Cells can be seen only under a microscope as they are very small.

The number of cells in each organism varies. There are certain organisms which are made up of a single cell. These organisms are called *unicellular* organisms. *Amoeba* and *Paramecium* are unicellular animals, while *Chlamydomonas* and *Euglena* are unicellular plants. Organisms which are made up of many cells are called *multicellular* organisms. For example, humans, fishes, ferns.

Activity 2

To study animal and plant cells.

Materials required An onion, tweezers, a glass slide, cover slips, iodine.

Method Take a small piece of onion. Peel off the thin film lining the inner surface. Place it on a slide using the tweezers. Put a drop of iodine to stain it and place a cover slip over it.

(Contd..,)

Now, lightly scrape the inner lining of your cheek with your finger and place the scrapings on a fresh slide, stain it and cover it with a cover slip.

Observe the two slides you have prepared under the microscope. You will see small compartment-like cells in both the slides [Fig. 7.16 (a) and (b)].

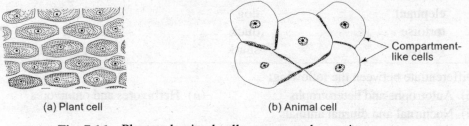

(a) Plant cell   (b) Animal cell

Fig. 7.16 Plant and animal cells as seen under a microscope

Growth

All living things show growth. Plants grow throughout their lives, while animals grow upto a certain period of time. Plants germinate from a seed and often grow upto hundreds of feet in height. Animals grow from a tiny egg into a complete individual. For example, an elephant grows from an egg, which is less than a millimetre in size, to become the largest animal on land.

 **Activity 3**

Materials required   Cotton, plate, peas.

Method   Take some wet cotton in a plate. Place a few peas on it. Sprinkle water on the cotton to keep it moist. After a day or two, you will observe that leaves and roots grow out of the peas (Fig. 7.17).

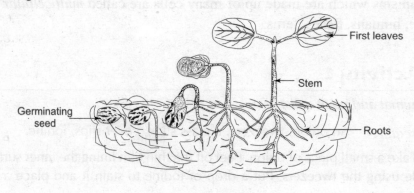

Fig. 7.17 Germination in pea

Nutrition

All living organisms require food for maintenance of life. A child grows by eating food, so do animals. Green plants can make their own food from simple raw materials. They have a green pigment called *chlorophyll* which helps them to trap solar energy. With the help of this solar energy, they convert carbon dioxide and water into food. This food is mainly in the form of glucose or sugars. The process by which they prepare food is called *photosynthesis* (Fig. 7.18). Animals cannot prepare their own food. They depend on plants or other animals for their nourishment.

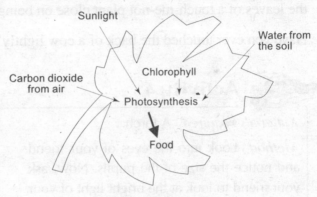

Fig. 7.18 Photosynthesis

Photosynthesis is the process by which green plants make food using carbon dioxide, water and solar energy.

Respiration

All living organisms respire. It involves the taking in of oxygen and giving out of carbon dioxide. During this process food, which is in the form of glucose, is burnt in the cells with the help of oxygen to release energy. Thus, respiration is a process by which food is broken down in the cell, with the help of oxygen, to release energy.

Excretion

All living things throw out the waste products produced in their bodies. Carbon dioxide, water vapour, urine, sweat, and faecal matter are the excretory products of humans and most animals. Plants excrete products like oxygen, gum, rubber, oils which are very useful to us and other animals. Eucalyptus oil and sandal wood oil are waste products too.

Lifespan

Living organisms have an average age upto which they generally live. Dogs and cats live for about twelve years, moths and flies for a day and microbes just for a few hours.

Some plants live only for a year, e.g., wheat, paddy, pea, gram; while there are plants which live for several years, e.g., mango, banyan, peepal, etc.

Response to stimuli

Living organisms are sensitive to various stimuli, i.e., they respond to changes in the environment, e.g., a plant grows towards light while an earthworm moves away from light, the leaves of a touch-me-not plant close on being touched.

Have you ever touched the back of a cow lightly? You will see that it will twitch.

Activity 4

Materials required A torch.

Method Look into the eyes of your friend and notice the size of the pupils. Now, ask your friend to look at the bright light of your torch. While he does so, notice his pupils again. Do you see any difference? The size of the pupil becomes smaller in bright light and bigger in dim light (Fig. 7.19).

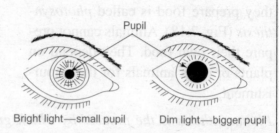

Bright light—small pupil   Dim light—bigger pupil

Fig. 7.19   An example of response to stimulus

Reproduction

All organisms have the ability to reproduce their own kind. Birds lay eggs which hatch to give chicks that grow into hens or cocks. Plants reproduce by producing seeds. The seedlings grow into new plants. Some plants reproduce by stems, e.g., money plant; some by roots, e.g., banana; some by leaves, e.g., *Bryophyllum* (Fig. 7.20).

The characteristics you have seen so far are common to both plants and animals, in fact, to all living organisms. However, plants are quite different from animals. Let us now see how they differ from each other (Table 7.2).

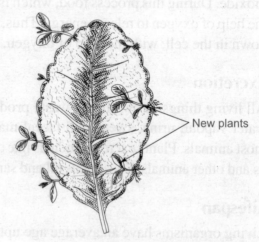

New plants

Fig. 7.20   *Bryophyllum* reproduces by leaves

Table 7.2   Differences between plants and animals

Plants	Animals
1. Generally plants prepare their own food by the process of photosynthesis. They do not depend on other organisms for their nutrition.	1. Animals cannot prepare their own food and hence, are dependent on other organisms for their nutrition.
2. Since they need not search for food, they do not move from place to place. However, a few lower plants do move, e.g., *Euglena* and *Chlamydomonas*.	2. They move from place to place in search of food and to protect themselves from enemies. However, corals and sea anemones do not move from place to place.
3. Growth in plants continues throughout life. It takes place mainly at the root and stem tips.	3. Growth takes place only upto a certain period. It takes place throughout the body of the organism.
4. Plants reproduce by producing seeds, spores, stems, leaves, or roots.	4. Animals reproduce by laying eggs or giving birth to live young ones.
5. Plants do not have specialized organs for excretion.	5. Animals generally have organs which help them to excrete. In humans, the lungs, skin, kidneys, and large intestine help in excretion.
6. Plants are less sensitive because they have no sense organs and no nervous system.	6. They are highly sensitive as they have sense organs and a nervous system.

 Recall

- Cell is the basic unit of life. Living organisms may be unicellular or multicellular.
- All living things grow from an infant stage to an adult.
- All organisms need food to sustain themselves.
- All organisms respire. During this process food is broken down with the help of oxygen to release energy.
- All organisms excrete—they throw out the waste products produced by the body.
- Living organisms live upto a certain age after which they die.
- All living organisms respond to various stimuli.
- All living organisms have the ability to reproduce their own kind.

Let's Answer

1. How do plants excrete?
2. Why do we close our eyes for a few moments when we step out of our house on a hot afternoon?
3. What do you understand by the term *lifespan*?
4. Give some points of difference between plants and animals with respect to growth and excretion.

NAMING OF LIVING ORGANISMS

In order to name plants and animals, scientists have classified organisms into distinct groups based on their similarities. In doing so, they kept certain points in mind—habit, habitat and the ability to interbreed to produce young ones.

In 1753, a scientist in Sweden named *Carolus Linnaeus* thought of an orderly system for *classifying plants and animals*. He grouped all organisms according to a two-part name (binomial). The first part of the name is the *generic* grouping or *genus*. The second part is the *specific* grouping or *species*. Scientists today still use this basic idea of his system, which is known as the *binomial system of classification*.

A genus consists of closely related, similar species, i.e., *Felis* is the generic name for the domestic cat, leopard, lion, etc. They are thick-furred and sharp-clawed with pointed teeth. So, they all belong to the same genus but cannot interbreed.

The second part identifies a particular species and is called the *specific name*. Organisms which have a similar habit and habitat, and can interbreed, belong to the same *species*. Plants and animals are often named after the country or place where they are found. Here are several examples which will help you to understand scientific naming.

Scientific name		Common name
Genus	*Species*	
Ficus	*bengalensis*	Banyan tree
Ficus	*religiosa*	Peepal tree
Ficus	*carica*	Fig tree

The trees belong to the same genus, *Ficus*, but are of different species.

Felis	*domesticus*	Domestic cat
Felis	*leo*	Lion
Felis	*leopardus*	Leopard

The cat, lion and the leopard are of the same genus but belong to different species.

Here are some more examples:

Scientific name		Common name
Genus	*Species*	
Allium	*sepa*	Onion
Allium	*sativum*	Garlic
Rosa	*indica*	Rose
Homo	*sapiens*	Human being
Rana	*tigrina*	Frog

The generic name always starts with a capital (upper case) letter and the specific name with a small (lower case) letter.

 Do You Know?

There are more than 8,600 species of plants all over the world and 1,20,000 species of animals and 3,00,000 species of birds. Many of these are being destroyed by human activities like hunting, cutting of trees, pollution, etc.

IMPORTANCE OF PLANTS AND ANIMALS

Plants are very useful to man. They are divided into various categories according to their uses:

1. Food → cereals, legumes, nuts, oil, sugar, vegetables and spices.
2. Fibre-yielding → cotton, flax, jute, hemp, coir.
3. Medicinal plants→ eucalyptus.
4. Beverages → Almost all beverages are obtained from plants, e.g., tea, coffee.
5. Wood, timber → e.g. teak, bamboo.
6. Ornamental plants → Rose, jasmine, cactus, money plant, etc.

Animals are also of great importance to us as they provide us with the following:

1. Food → milk, meat, egg, honey, fish.
2. Fibres → Wool from sheep skin and silk from silkworm.
3. Ornaments → Pearls and corals, ivory.
4. Agricultural purpose → Cow, buffalo.
5. Transportation → Bullock or horse cart.
6. Fuel → Cow dung cakes and also biogas from animal excreta.
7. With the help of some microbes we can get curd from milk and vinegar by fermentation.

8. Microbes play a very important role in the production of some medicines.
9. Animals such as the cow are used for operating rollers to expel oil from seeds and to draw water from the well.

Harmful Plants and Animals

Some plants can be harmful to us. Given below are a few examples.
1. Parthenium causes skin irritation and even asthma (in some cases).
2. Parasitic plants like dodders suck nutrition from the host plant.
3. Some plants multiply at a fast rate and affect the growth of the main crop.
4. Many harmful drugs like cocaine, hashish and marijuana are obtained from plants.

Some unicellular microbes like bacteria, virus, and protozoa cause diseases in plants and animals. Smut and rust are plant diseases, whereas influenza, tuberculosis, cholera, malaria, dysentery are examples of animal diseases caused by micro-organisms.

 Recall

- A scientific name has two parts. The first part gives the generic name and the second part gives the specific name or name of the species.
- Species are a group of organisms which have similar habits and can interbreed.
- A genus consists of closely related, similar species.
- Both plants and animals are very useful to man as a source of food, medicines, fibre, etc.
- There are, however, plant and animal species which are harmful and cause diseases in other plants and animals including man.

EXERCISES

1. **Choose the appropriate answer**
   (i) Which of the following is an invertebrate?
      (a) Lizard   (b) Sparrow
      (c) Frog   (d) Spider
   (ii) Which one of the following is a mammal?
      (a) Fish   (b) Mouse
      (c) Bird   (d) Snake
   (iii) Most plants are
      (a) heterotrophic   (b) autotrophic
      (c) saprophytic   (d) none of the above
   (iv) Which of the following plants have roots, stems and leaves?
      (a) Ferns   (b) Fungi
      (c) Mosses   (d) Algae

(v) A mango tree belongs to the group of
    (a) algae
    (b) flowering plants
    (c) fungi
    (d) ferns

(vi) Which of the following is a vertebrate?
    (a) Octopus
    (b) Starfish
    (c) Snail
    (d) Monkey

2. **Mark the following sentences as *True* or *False***
    (a) Plants prepare their own food.
    (b) Omnivores eat only fish.
    (c) Diurnal animals are active at night.
    (d) Xerophytes are plants that live in deserts.
    (e) Snake is a vertebrate.
    (f) Shrubs are small plants.
    (g) Perennial plants live for many years.
    (h) A group of individuals is known as a species.

3. **Fill in the blanks**
    (a) _____ is a unicellular organism.
    (b) Fishes respire through _____.
    (c) Amphibians, reptiles, birds, and mammals respire with the help of _____.
    (d) _____ is a moving plant.
    (e) _____ is a stationary animal.
    (f) _____ is a parasite.
    (g) Frog is to a vertebrate what a _____ is to an invertebrate.
    (h) Lion is to a den what a monkey is to a _____.

4. **Match the columns**

A	B
(a) Mushroom	(i) Vertebrates
(b) Palm tree	(ii) Non-flowering plants
(c) Feathers	(iii) Birds
(d) Animals with backbone	(iv) Flowering plants

5. **Give one word answer for the following**
    (i) Name a plant which is a saprophyte.
    (ii) Name the group of plants with long roots and thin leaves.
    (iii) Some animals and plants feed on other living things. What are they called?
    (iv) Which of these grow throughout their life—plants or animals?
    (v) What is a group of similar animals known as?
    (vi) Some living organisms prepare their own food. What are they called?

6. **Classify the following as herbs, shrubs, or trees**
    (a) Neem
    (b) Rose
    (c) Tulsi
    (d) Coconut
    (e) Carrot
    (f) Jasmine

7. **Give the scientific names of the following**
   (a) Humans   (b) Indian tiger   (c) Mango

8. **Name the habitat of the following**
   (a) Cockroach   (b) Coconut tree   (c) Cactus
   (d) Monkey   (e) Crocodile

9. **Answer in brief**
   (a) Why are living things classified?
   (b) Classify the flowering plants according to their shape and size.
   (c) What are microbes? How can they help us?
   (d) What are parasitic animals? What harm do they cause?
   (e) Differentiate between annual and biennial plants.
   (f) Define vertebrates. Give three examples from the animals you see around you.
   (g) Define invertebrates. Give three examples which you commonly see.
   (h) What do we understand by the habitat of an animal or a plant?
   (i) Differentiate between (i) living and non-living organisms (ii) plants and animals.
   (j) Why are animals dependent on plants for their food?
   (k) What do you mean by heterotrophs and autotrophs?
   (l) Plants do not eat food. Where do they get their food from?
   (m) What is a scientific name and why do we use it?
   (n) Define species.
   (o) With the help of a simple experiment, prove that plants prepare starch during the process of photosynthesis.

THINK AND ANSWER

Name the characteristic shown by living things in the following examples:
(a) The cat runs away when hit by a stone.
(b) Though people die, the world population is on the increase.
(c) The chick becomes a hen in a few weeks.
(e) A child cries when it is hungry.
(f) If you keep a mouse in a small jar with its lid closed, it will die after some time.

 Teacher's Notes

- Classes can be taken in the school garden and the students can acquaint themselves with the different varieties of plants and animals, e.g. insects, found in the garden.
- The class can be divided into groups. Each group can do a project on:
  - Plants and animals that live in water.
  - Vertebrates and invertebrates.
  - Features of the plant kingdom such as shape and size, food, habit and habitat.
  - Features of the animal kingdom on the same lines as for plants.

8

- Parts of a typical plant
- The root system—tap root and fibrous root
- The shoot system—stem and leaf
- Flower
- Fruit
- Seed

Structure and Function of Plants

The living world is divided into the plant and the animal kingdoms. As already learnt in chapter 7, both plants and animals have some common characteristics which define them as living beings. Let us now take up the structure and function of plants first in detail.

PARTS OF A TYPICAL PLANT

All plants can be divided into the *flowering* or the *non-flowering types*. Let us take a typical flowering plant and study its parts. The body of the plant consists of two systems—*the root system* and *the shoot system* (Fig. 8.1).

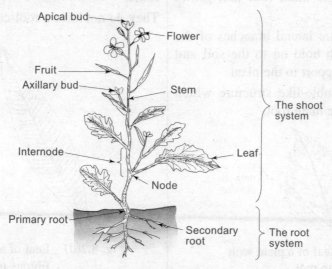

Apical bud

Flower

Fruit

Axillary bud

Stem

The shoot system

Internode

Leaf

Node

Primary root

Secondary root

The root system

Fig. 8.1   Parts of a typical flowering plant

ROOT SYSTEM

The root system is generally found under the soil. The root is pale, creamish-brown in colour. It bears no leaves or buds. There are two types of root systems [Fig. 8.2(a) and (b)]:

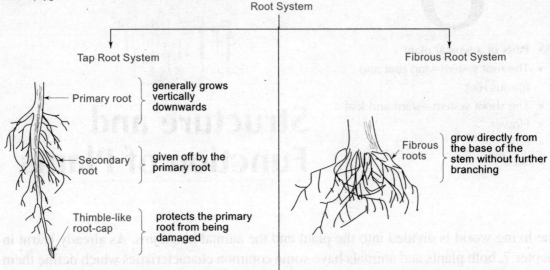

Fig. 8.2(a) The tap root system

Fig. 8.2(b) The fibrous root system

Examples of plants having tap roots are mango, neem, pea, etc.

Tap roots generally grow vertically downwards and give off lateral branches from the main root.

Primary root is the main root that grows downwards.

Secondary roots are lateral branches of the primary root which hold on to the soil and give mechanical support to the plant.

Root-cap is a thimble-like structure which covers the tip of the main root.

Examples of plants having fibrous roots are sugarcane, maize, wheat, etc.

Fibrous roots generally grow in clusters of slender roots from the base of the stem.

There are no separate primary or secondary roots.

They do not have a root-cap.

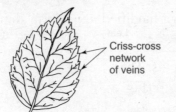

Fig. 8.2(c) Leaf of a plant with tap root

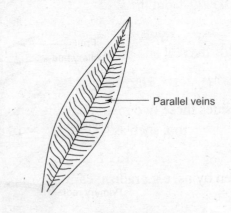

Fig. 8.2(d) Leaf of a plant with fibrous roots

Plants with the tap root system bear leaves which are generally broad and have a criss-cross network of veins [Fig. 8.2 (c)].	Plants with the fibrous root system bear leaves which are long and tapering and have parallel veins [Fig. 8.2 (d)].

Activity 1

To observe tap and fibrous roots.

Materials required Rajma or gram seeds, maize seeds, Petri dishes.

Method Take rajma, or any other gram, and maize seeds. Soak them in water in two different Petri dishes. Allow them to germinate for 2–3 days. Observe the roots that grow out of the seeds. These will belong to either of the types shown in Figure 8.2. Find out which seed grows which type of root.

Activity 2

To observe the types of veins in different leaves.

Materials required Leaves of corn, bean, mango, maize; sheets of paper.

Method Collect leaves of corn, bean, mango, maize. Trace out their outline on a white sheet of paper. Observe the veins in the leaves of these plants. You will see that in some leaves the veins form a criss-cross network [Fig. 8.2 (c)], while in some the veins are parallel to each other [Fig. 8.2 (d)].

Functions of Roots

Roots perform major functions such as *providing support* to the plant and *absorption of materials* from the soil.

Support   Roots give support to the plant. It anchors the plant firmly to the ground. It also holds the soil and prevents it from being washed away easily.

Absorption   They help in the absorption of water and minerals through the root hairs.

Besides these two major functions, roots are often modified to perform some *additional functions* too, such as,

Storage of food   Roots store food in certain plants. These modified roots are generally eaten by us, e.g., radish, carrot, turnip, sweet potato (Fig. 8.3).

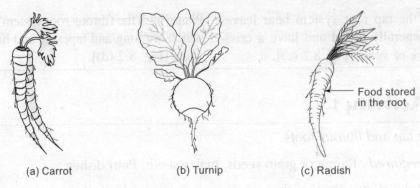

(a) Carrot   (b) Turnip   (c) Radish

Fig. 8.3   Modification of root as a storage organ

Respiration   Some plants growing in marshy regions have secondary roots coming out of the soil. These roots are highly porous and help in respiration. They are known as *pneumatophores*, e.g., that of *Rhizophora*. These are seen in plenty in Sunderbans, West Bengal (Fig. 8.4).

Mechanical support   In some plants like banyan, branches give out roots which grow downwards, towards the soil. These roots help in supporting the heavy branches, and are called *prop roots* (Fig. 8.5).

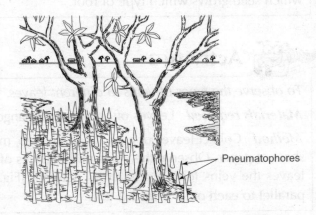

Fig. 8.4   Pneumatophores seen in marshy places

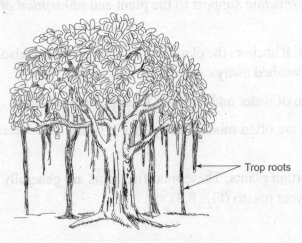

Fig. 8.5   Prop roots of banyan

Fig. 8.6   Stilt roots of screwpine

Some other plants like maize and screwpine have long and thin stems. Such stems require additional support. They give out roots from the stem which support the plant (Fig. 8.6). Such roots are called *stilt roots*.

Recall

- Plants have two main systems—the root system and the shoot system.
- The tap root has a primary root, secondary roots and the root-cap.
- Fibrous roots have no primary or secondary roots and are without a root-cap.
- The main functions of a root are absorption of water and minerals, providing support to the plant and preventing the soil from being washed away.
- The other functions of certain modified roots are providing support, helping in respiration and storing of food.

Let's Answer

1. What are tap roots?
2. What are fibrous roots?
3. What are the two main systems of the plant?
4. What are pneumatophores?

SHOOT SYSTEM

The portion of the plant above the soil is called the *shoot system*. It consists of stems, leaves, flowers, and fruits (See Fig. 8.1).

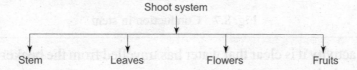

THE STEM

The stem grows upwards, towards light. It is generally erect and almost cylindrical in shape in most plants. A soft green stem is known as a *herbaceous stem*. In trees, the stem is quite thick and is covered with bark. It is brown in colour and is called the *trunk*.

Lateral offshoots from the stem are known as *branches*.

Nodes and Internodes In a herbaceous stem, the leaves are attached to the stem. The point of attachment is called the *node*. Nodes are seen at regular intervals. The space between any two nodes is called an *internode*.

Buds The tip of the stem bears *terminal* and *apical buds* which help in the growth of the stem. Buds are also present in the axil of the stem. These are called *axillary buds*.

Functions of the Stem

The two main functions of the stem are conduction of materials and providing support to the other parts of the shoot system.

Activity 3

To study conduction of materials by the stem.

Materials required A freshly cut leaf twig, water, red ink, beaker.

Method Take the leaf twig and place it in a beaker of water. Add a few drops of red ink to the water. Allow the setup to remain for a day. You will observe that the red colour spreads to all the parts of the twig (Fig. 8.7). The leaves show streaks of red.

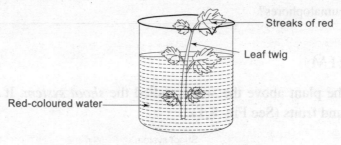

Fig. 8.7   Conduction in stem

Thus, from this activity it is clear that water has travelled from the beaker to different parts of the twig, through the stem.

Conduction The most important function of the stem is to transport materials. The stem transports water and minerals from the roots to the other parts of the plant. Again, it conducts prepared food from the leaves to all parts of the plant body.

Support The stem bears and supports the branches, leaves, flowers, and fruits. It spreads out the leaves in such a way that they get maximum sunlight. The *xylem* and *phloem* tissues in the stem help to hold the stem upright.

Just like the root, the stem also has some *additional functions*, namely, storage, food production, and climbing.

Storage   Stems, in some cases, are modified to store food. These are generally found underground. Onion, potato and ginger are very good examples [Fig. 8.8 (a), (b) and (c)]. In cactus, the stem also stores water and is found above the ground. In sugarcane, like in cactus, the stem is above the ground but stores prepared food.

Food production   In some cases, the stem does the function of the leaf, i.e., preparation of food. Such stems are therefore green in colour, e.g., cactus, prickly pear, etc. (Fig. 8.9).

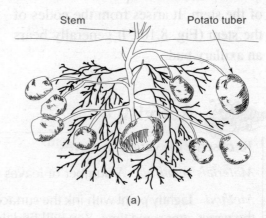

Fig. 8.8 (a)   Underground stem of potato

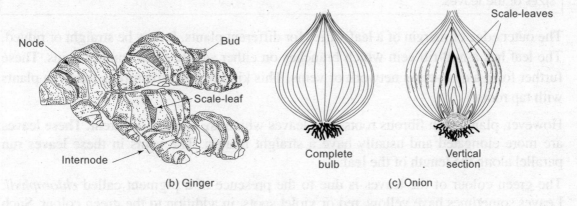

(b) Ginger

(c) Onion

Fig. 8.8 (b) and (c)   Underground stems of ginger and onion

Climbing   In a few plants, as in climbers, the stems are weak and cannot grow upwards on their own. The stems of these plants develop slender outgrowths called *tendrils*. These tendrils coil around neighbouring trees or objects for support as the plant climbs upwards, e.g., grape vine and passion flower.

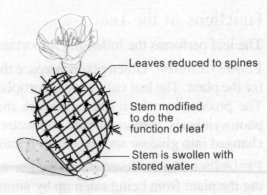

Leaves reduced to spines

Stem modified to do the function of leaf

Stem is swollen with stored water

Fig. 8.9   Cactus

THE LEAF

The leaf is a thin, expanded outgrowth of the stem. It arises from the nodes of the stem (Fig. 8.10). It generally bears an axillary bud.

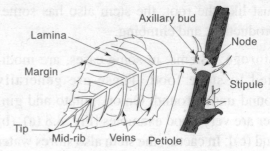

Fig. 8.10 The external structure of a leaf

 **Activity 4**

To observe the variety in leaves.

Materials required A number of leaves of different types, white paper, ink.

Method Lightly paint with ink the surface of a leaf and place a paper on top of it. Peel off the paper after some time. You will find the leaf-print on the paper. Compare the different leaf-prints. Observe the different margins, patterns of veins and the different shapes and sizes of the leaves.

The outer edge or margin of a leaf varies for different plants. It may be straight or ridged. The leaf has a mid-rib vein which branches on either side to form smaller veins. These further form a criss-cross network of veins. This kind of leaf structure is found in plants with tap roots.

However, plants with fibrous roots bear leaves which are slightly different. These leaves are more elongated and usually have a straight margin. The veins in these leaves run parallel along the length of the leaf.

The green colour of the leaves is due to the presence of a pigment called *chlorophyll*. Leaves sometimes have yellow, red or violet spots, in addition to the green colour. Such leaves are called *variegated leaves*.

Functions of the Leaf

The leaf performs the following important functions:

Photosynthesis Green plants prepare their own food and the leaves serve as the kitchen for the plant. The leaf cells have chloroplasts which contain a green pigment, chlorophyll. The process by which plants prepare their own food is called *photosynthesis*. During photosynthesis, carbon dioxide and water, in the presence of sunlight and chlorophyll, is changed into glucose and oxygen is released.

Protection In the desert plants the leaves are modified into spines. They help in protecting the plant from being eaten up by animals, e.g., *Opuntia*, *cactus*.

130

Respiration   There are tiny pores called *stomata* on the surface of the leaves. These can be seen under the microscope. Stomata help in taking in oxygen and giving out carbon dioxide. Thus, they function as respiratory organs.

Transpiration   The excess water in the plant is given out through the stomata in the form of water vapour. The process by which the plant continuously loses water is called *transpiration*. In desert plants the spines also help to reduce the loss of water.

 Activity 5

Materials required   Potted plant, plastic bag, some grease.

Method   Take a potted plant and grease both the sides of any one leaf. Place a plastic bag around the leaf and tie the open end. Place a plastic bag over a second leaf with no grease on it. After sometime compare the water droplets collected in both the plastic bags (Fig. 8.11). You will observe that the bag covering the ungreased leaf has a lot of water droplets as the leaf is able to transpire. The greased leaf is unable to transpire as its stomata are blocked by grease.

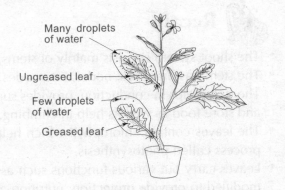

Many droplets of water

Ungreased leaf

Few droplets of water

Greased leaf

Fig. 8.11   Experiment to demonstrate transpiration

Leaves are also sometimes modified to perform some *additional functions* as given below.

Nutrition   Leaves, in some cases, are modified to trap insects, e.g., pitcher plant (Fig. 8.12), sundew, etc. These plants are called *insectivorous* plants.

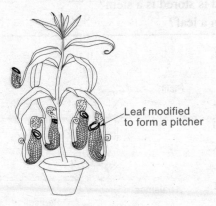

Leaf modified to form a pitcher

Fig. 8.12   Pitcher plant

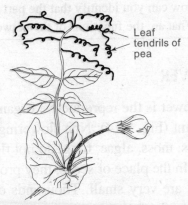

Leaf tendrils of pea

Fig. 8.13   Leaf tendrils in a pea plant

Climbing In sweet pea, the leaf gets modified into slender tendrils (Fig. 8.13). Tendrils coil around any support and help the plant to climb. In such plants, the stem is generally slender and weak.

Do You Know?

Non-stop leaves
The leaves of most plants grow to a maximum size and stop. But the leaves of *Welwitschia mirabilis* never stop growing. This plant grows in the Namibian desert of Southern Africa.

Recall

- The shoot system consists mainly of stems, leaves, flowers, and fruits.
- The stem has branches, nodes, internodes, and buds.
- The stem helps in conduction, provides support and, sometimes, is modified to produce and store food as well as help in climbing.
- The leaves contain chlorophyll which helps the plants to prepare their own food by a process called photosynthesis.
- Leaves carry out various functions such as respiration, transpiration and are sometimes modified to provide protection, nutrition and support.

Let's Answer

1. How can you demonstrate experimentally the transportation of water in plants?
2. Name two plants in which the food is stored in the stem.
3. How can you identify that the part in which food is stored is a stem?
4. What are the functions of the network of veins in a leaf?

FLOWER

The flower is the reproductive organ in a flowering plant (Fig. 8.14). Non-flowering plants such as ferns, moss, algae, fungi do not flower or bear seeds. In the place of seeds, they produce spores. Spores are very small. Thousands of them look like a speck of dust.

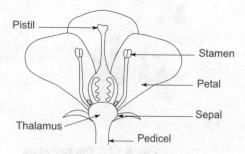

Fig. 8.14 A typical flower

Features of a Flower

A complete flower shows the following parts:

(a) The flower is borne on a stalk called the *pedicel*.

(b) The pedicel is swollen on the uppermost part and this portion is called the *thalamus*.

(c) The thalamus bears the four whorls of the flower:

    (i) sepals   (ii) petals   (iii) stamen   (iv) pistil

Whorls of a Flower

The flower consists of the following four whorls:

Sepals   They form the outermost whorl of the flower [Fig. 8.15(a)]. Sepals are usually green in colour but in a few cases may be differently coloured (e.g. gulmohur). They protect the flower during the bud stage.

       Fig. 8.15(a)   Sepals   **Fig. 8.15(b)**   Petals

Petals   They are often brightly coloured. During the bud stage they protect the inner parts of the flower [Fig. 8.15 (b)]. When the flower opens, the bright petals serve to attract insects which help in pollination (transfer of the pollen grains from the anther to the stigma).

Stamens (Male sex organ)   They are usually 4–6 in number. A stamen consists of an *anther* attached to the tip of a tubular *filament* [Fig. 8.15(c)]. The anther contains the male sex cells—the pollen grains.

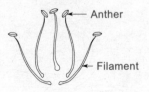

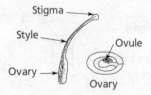

      Fig. 8.15(c)   A stamen   **Fig. 8.15(d)**   Pistil

Pistil (Female sex organ)   The pistil is also called the *carpel*. This is the innermost part of the flower [Fig. 8.15(d)]. The pistil is divided into,

the *stigma* which receives the pollen grains,

133

the *style* which is the tube through which pollen grains travel down to the ovary,

the *ovary* which contains the ovules, and

the *ovules* which are the female sex cells.

A flower thus consists of sepals, petals, stamen, and pistil (carpel). Most flowers bear both stamens and pistils. In some, however, only pistils or only stamens may be present.

Functions of a Flower

The flower performs the following important functions:

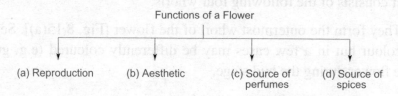

Functions of a Flower

(a) Reproduction   (b) Aesthetic   (c) Source of perfumes   (d) Source of spices

Process of Reproduction   The formation of a new seed begins when a male sex cell of the pollen grain fuses with a female sex cell in the ovule. The process of reproduction involves the following steps:

(i) *Pollination*   The transfer of the pollen grain from the anther to the stigma is called *pollination* [Fig. 8.16(a)]. It marks the beginning of the process of reproduction. First the anther ripens and the pollen sacs split open to release the pollen grains. This pollen is then carried to the stigma by wind, insects or other sources.

(ii) *Fertilization*   After the pollen lands on the stigma, the next step called *fertilization* [Fig. 8.16(b)] takes place. The male sex cell in the pollen unites with the female sex cell in the ovule.

After they unite, the ovule becomes a *seed*. The ovary becomes a *fruit*. Petals and sepals die and wither out.

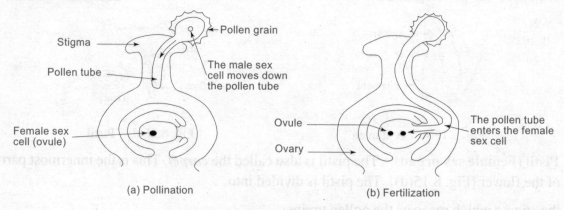

Fig. 8.16   Process of reproduction

This type of reproduction where a male cell unites with a female cell is called *sexual reproduction*. This requires a male and a female parent. However, many plants can also reproduce in another way which requires only one parent, e.g., money plant, *Bougainvillea*, rose, jasmine. In these, a part of the stem gives rise to a new plant. In banana, the roots give rise to new saplings and in *Bryophyllum*, the leaves give off young plants. This type of reproduction is called *vegetative reproduction*. In general, such type of reproduction involving only one parent is known as *asexual reproduction*.

Aesthetic   Plants are grown in gardens, parks, road sides, and in our houses for decoration purposes. Cut and dried flowers are used for interior decoration.

Source of Perfumes   Rose, lavender, jasmine, etc., yield perfumes or scents. Today aroma therapy plays a big role in curing many diseases.

Source of Spices   For example, dried flower buds of the clove plant are used as a spice as well as in medicines.

FRUIT

A fruit is defined *as a matured ovary in which the ovules have turned into seeds* (Fig. 8.17). The following functions are associated with a fruit:
(a) storage of food
(b) dispersal of seeds
(c) protection of the seed

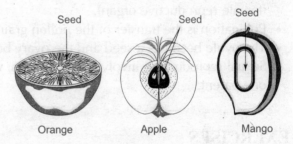

Fig. 8.17   Different type of fruits

SEED

Peas, beans, grams are all seeds (Fig. 8.18).

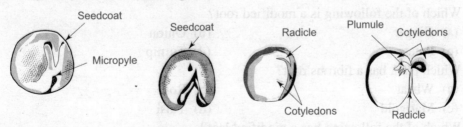

Fig. 8.18   Seeds

Soak some gram seeds in water. After 2–3 days you will observe drops of water coming out from a small hole at the pointed end. This small hole is called the *micropyle*. Now remove the outer brown cover which is the *seed coat*. Split the seed carefully. The two parts are called *cotyledons*. In between the two cotyledons observe a light yellow structure which is the *embryo*. This develops into a new plant.

(a) Radicle → grows into root

(b) Plumule → grows into shoot

Do You Know?

Corpse flower, *Rafflesia*, is a parasitic plant that grows in the forests of South East Asia. It has the largest flower with the strongest smell in the world.

Recall

- The flower is the reproductive organ in a flowering plant.
- The main parts of a flower are sepals, petals, stamen (male reproductive organ) and pistil (female reproductive organ).
- Pollination is the transfer of the pollen grains from the anther to the stigma.
- The ovule becomes a seed and the ovary becomes a fruit.
- Sexual reproduction involves two parents, whereas asexual reproduction involves only one parent.

EXERCISES

1. **Choose the appropriate answer**

    (i) Which part of the flower turns into the fruit?

        (a) Petals   (b) Sepals

        (c) Ovary   (d) Stamens

    (ii) Which of the following is a modified root?

        (a) Ginger   (b) Onion

        (c) Potato   (d) Turnip

    (iii) Which plant has a fibrous root?

        (a) Wheat   (b) Rose

        (c) Marigold   (d) Tulsi

    (iv) Which of the following has a modified leaf?

        (a) Banyan   (b) Cactus

        (c) Maize   (d) Sugarcane

2. **Mark the following sentences as** *True* **or** *False*

   (a) Wheat is a monocotyledonous seed.

   (b) Maize grain is called a fruit.

   (c) Root absorbs water and minerals from the soil.

   (d) Leaves can manufacture food without sunlight.

   (e) Food is only stored in fruits in the plants.

   (f) Plumule of an embryo develops into the stem.

   (g) Roots have nodes and internodes.

   (h) Stems of all plants stand erect.

3. **Fill in the blanks**

   (a) Photosynthesis takes place in plants with the help of the pigment _____.

   (b) Leaves of _____ plants are modified to trap their prey.

   (c) The _____ of a flower changes into a seed after fertilization.

   (d) During pollination pollen grains are transferred from the _____ to the _____ of the flower.

   (e) Vegetative reproduction is a kind of _____ reproduction.

   (f) Leaves with patches of different colours are known as _____ leaves.

4. **Match the following columns**

   (a) Root-cap   (i) Parallel veins

   (b) Fibrous roots   (ii) Respiration

   (c) Carrot   (iii) Protection

   (d) Pneumatophores   (iv) Stem

   (e) Ginger   (v) Root

5. **Give one word for the following**

   (a) Name the part of the stamen, which produces pollen grains.

   (b) What is the outer edge of a leaf called?

   (c) Name the bud present at the tip of a stem.

   (d) Give an example of a plant with fibrous roots.

   (e) Is the fleshy underground part of the potato plant a root or a stem?

   (f) What are the roots that grow from the branches of a banyan tree called?

   (g) Which part of the pistil forms the fruit?

6. **Short answer questions**

   (a) Name the different parts of the plant as marked.

   (b) Which plant organ makes food?

   (c) Which plant organ is needed for reproduction?

   (d) Which plant organ carries water to the leaves?

   (e) What kind of root does this plant have?

7. **Give examples for the following**
   (a) Two stems that we eat.
   (b) Two seeds that we eat.
   (c) Two modified roots that we eat.
   (d) Two modified stems that we eat.

8. **Answer the following questions briefly**
   (a) Define pollination.
   (b) Draw the carpel and label its parts.
   (c) What are the functions of the petals and sepals?
   (d) Differentiate between pollination and fertilization.
   (e) When the roots of a plant are damaged, the plant dies. Explain why?
   (f) Why are onion and potato said to be stems though they are found underground?
   (g) Give three examples each of plants having fibrous and tap roots.
   (h) Make a list of vegetables you eat. Classify them into stem, root, leaf, flower, fruit, and seed.
   (i) What is a thalamus? What is its function?
   (j) Why does cactus have a thick green stem with spines?
   (k) Which parts of the flower form the fruit and the seed?
   (l) Which part of the embryo develops (a) into the root and (b) into the shoot?
   (m) Name the plant in which (a) stem is modified as tendril (b) leaf is modified as tendril.
   (n) What are variegated leaves? Give examples.
   (o) How is vegetative reproduction different from sexual reproduction?

9. **Answer the following questions in detail**
   (i) Explain the following
      (a) photosynthesis (b) transpiration (c) pollination (d) fertilization
   (ii) What are the main and additional functions of the following?
      (a) root (b) stem (c) leaf (d) flower
   (iii) How are certain parts of the plants modified?
   (iv) Distinguish between:
      (a) Prop root and stilt root
      (b) Stamen and pistil
      (c) Tap root and fibrous root
      (d) Simple leaf and compound leaf

THINK AND ANSWER

Some vegetables are actually fruits. Find out the difference between fruits and vegetables. Name one real vegetable and two false fruits.

Teacher's Notes

- A small plant can be brought to the class to show its various parts.
- Samples of different modified stems and roots can be shown in class.

138

9

- Digestive system
- Respiratory system
- Circulatory system
- Nervous system
- Excretory system
- Muscular system
- Skeletal system
- Reproductive system

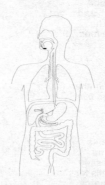

Structure and Function of Animals

All organisms perform certain basic functions such as breathing, excretion, reproduction, etc. They possess various organs to perform these functions. These organs combine to form different organ systems and each organ system performs one major function in the body.

In the following sections we shall learn about the important organ systems in animals, especially in the human body.

DIGESTIVE SYSTEM

In a car, fuel is burnt to produce energy which makes the car run. Similarly, the food that we eat provides us with the energy to carry out various activities such as movement, reproduction, etc. So, all organisms need to eat food as it is the only source of energy.

Most animals take in food through the mouth. However, this food cannot be used as such by the body cells. It has to be converted into a simpler and more soluble form which is easily absorbed by the body.

The process by which food is converted into a simple and soluble form is called digestion. This process is carried out by the *digestive system*. The various parts of the digestive system and their specific functions are shown in Figure 9.1.

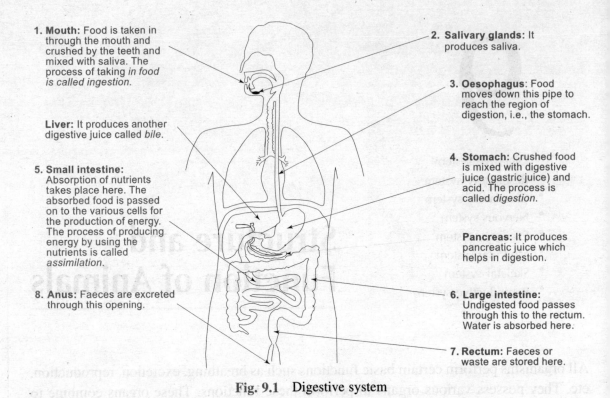

1. **Mouth:** Food is taken in through the mouth and crushed by the teeth and mixed with saliva. The process of taking *in food is called ingestion.*

Liver: It produces another digestive juice called *bile.*

5. **Small intestine:** Absorption of nutrients takes place here. The absorbed food is passed on to the various cells for the production of energy. The process of producing energy by using the nutrients is called *assimilation.*

8. **Anus:** Faeces are excreted through this opening.

2. **Salivary glands:** It produces saliva.

3. **Oesophagus:** Food moves down this pipe to reach the region of digestion, i.e., the stomach.

4. **Stomach:** Crushed food is mixed with digestive juice (gastric juice) and acid. The process is called *digestion.*

Pancreas: It produces pancreatic juice which helps in digestion.

6. **Large intestine:** Undigested food passes through this to the rectum. Water is absorbed here.

7. **Rectum:** Faeces or waste are stored here.

Fig. 9.1   Digestive system

The mouth consists of teeth which help in mixing and crushing the food and a tongue which identifies the taste. Humans have two different sets of teeth. Children upto the age of eight have 20 *milk teeth*. These are later replaced by 32 *permanent teeth* in the adults (Fig. 9.2).

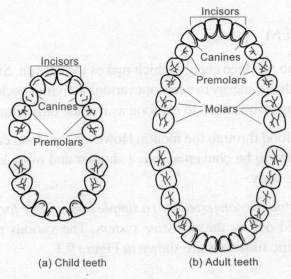

(a) Child teeth   (b) Adult teeth

Fig. 9.2   Teeth arrangement in a child and an adult

The tongue helps in mixing and swallowing the food, tasting things and, above all, in speech.

Put drops of different solutions, say, of sugar, salt, lemon, and quinine on your tongue. You will find that they all taste different. This is because the tongue has four different taste areas. And a particular taste can be identified only in the area meant for that taste (Fig. 9.3).

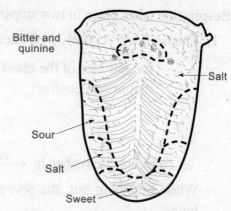

Fig. 9.3   Taste areas of a tongue

RESPIRATORY SYSTEM

We all use energy to do different kinds of work. We get this energy when food is broken down during the process of respiration (Fig. 9.4).

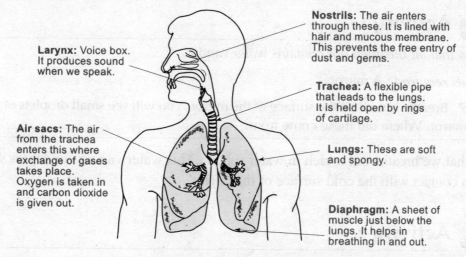

Larynx: Voice box. It produces sound when we speak.

Air sacs: The air from the trachea enters this where exchange of gases takes place. Oxygen is taken in and carbon dioxide is given out.

Nostrils: The air enters through these. It is lined with hair and mucous membrane. This prevents the free entry of dust and germs.

Trachea: A flexible pipe that leads to the lungs. It is held open by rings of cartilage.

Lungs: These are soft and spongy.

Diaphragm: A sheet of muscle just below the lungs. It helps in breathing in and out.

Fig. 9.4   Respiratory system

Respiration

During the process of respiration, the following process takes place.

Food
+ oxygen
(which we breathe in)   →   Energy + water vapour
+ carbon dioxide
(which we breathe out)

Respiration takes place in two steps:

1. The *first step* is purely a physical process of breathing in and out of air by the lungs.

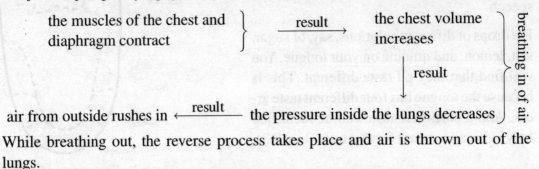

While breathing out, the reverse process takes place and air is thrown out of the lungs.

2. The *second step* involves the burning of food with the help of the oxygen that we breathe in, to produce energy. This takes place within the cell and is therefore called *cellular respiration*.

 ## Activity 1

To show that air breathed out contains water vapour.

Materials required   A mirror.

Method   Breathe out air on the surface of the mirror. You will see small droplets of water on the mirror. Where did these come from?

The air that we breathe out is rich in water vapour. This water vapour condenses when it comes in contact with the cold surface of the mirror.

 ## Activity 2

To show that air breathed out contains carbon dioxide.

Materials required   Limewater, glass tumbler, straw.

Method   Take limewater (calcium hydroxide) in a glass tumbler and blow air into it through a straw. Then shake it. The limewater turns milky (Fig. 9.5).

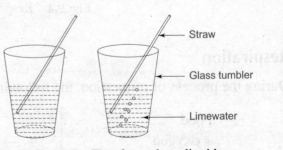

Fig. 9.5   Test for carbon dioxide

The air that you breathe out is rich in carbon dioxide. This reacts with the limewater to form an insoluble substance, calcium carbonate. So, the limewater turns milky.

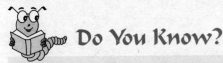
At the back of the throat is a small flap called *epiglottis* which closes off the windpipe when we eat, so that the food does not enter it (Fig. 9.6). If food enters the trachea or the windpipe, we choke and cough as the chest muscles contract violently to get rid of the blockage.

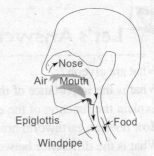

Fig. 9.6 Showing epiglottis

In lower animals the process of breathing takes place quite differently. Fishes take in oxygen through their *gills*. Insects have small openings on the sides of their body called *spiracles*. These lead into the trachea and traverse throughout the body. Earthworm breathes through the *skin*. Can you now guess why we see so many earthworms on the surface of the soil after it rains? (Fig. 9.7 and Fig. 9.8)

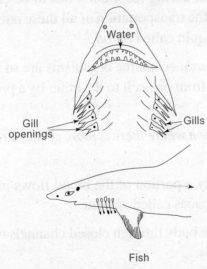

Fig. 9.7 Gills in fish

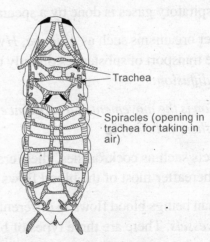

Fig. 9.8 Spiracles in insects

Recall

- The human body consists of several organ systems.
- The digestive system consists of (i) mouth (ii) oesophagus (iii) stomach (iv) small intestine (v) large intestine (vi) rectum and (vii) anus.
- The glands associated with the digestive system are the salivary glands, liver and pancreas.
- The respiratory system consists of (i) nostrils (ii) nasal cavity (iii) pharynx (iv) trachea (v) bronchi (vi) lungs.

Let's Answer

1. What are alveoli?
2. What is the importance of the diaphragm?
3. Explain the function of the epiglottis.
4. How does an earthworm breathe?
5. What is the difference between the milk teeth and the permanent teeth?

CIRCULATORY SYSTEM

In animals the food taken in is digested and absorbed in the small intestine. The absorbed nutrients are then transported to other parts of the body where they are utilized for various purposes. Similarly, oxygen that is taken into the lungs has to be transported to all the body tissues for respiration, and carbon dioxide given out during respiration has to be carried back from the cells to the lungs. In most organisms the transportation of all these nutrients and respiratory gases is done by a special type of liquid called *blood*.

In lower organisms such as *Amoeba*, *Hydra*, and *Paramecium* the organisms are so small that the transport of substances directly takes place from one cell to the other by a process called *diffusion*.

Diffusion is the movement of a substance from a region where there is more of it to a region where there is less of it.

In insects such as cockroaches, flies, crab, etc., only a portion of the blood flows in vessels. Thereafter most of the blood flows freely in spaces called *sinuses*.

In human beings blood flows to different parts of the body through closed channels called *blood vessels*. There are three types of blood vessels.

Arteries carry oxygenated blood (containing oxygen) to different parts of the body. They are thick-walled and deep set in our body.

Veins carry deoxygenated blood (blood without oxygen but with carbon dioxide) collected from different parts of the body. They are located just below the skin.

Capillaries are thin-walled and connect the arteries and the veins.

The blood vessels, together with the heart, constitute the circulatory system.

Heart

The heart is located in the middle with the lower end towards the left portion of the chest cavity. It pumps blood through the blood vessels to all the cells in the body (Fig. 9.9). If you hold the inside of your wrist you can feel a regular twitching movement. This is called the *pulse*.

The pulse is felt because the blood rushes through the arteries each time the heart pumps it out. Thus, each beat of the heart causes a pulse in the artery. The heartbeat and pulse have the same rhythm.

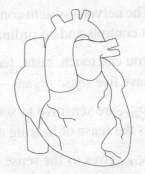

Fig. 9.9 Human heart

 ## Activity 3

To feel your pulse.

There are various places on the body where the pulse can be felt. They are at the temple, wrist and neck. With the help of your teacher find the pulse of your partner. Count the number of pulse beats per minute.

Now ask your partner to do the same for you and again count the pulse. You can tabulate the pulse rates of your other classmates as well. In most cases you will find it to be 82–84 beats per minute.

A *stethoscope* is an instrument which is used to listen to the sound of the heartbeat. You can make a simple stethoscope by attaching a rubber tube to a funnel (Fig. 9.10). Place the funnel end on the chest and listen through the other tube end. You will hear the regular beats of the heart.

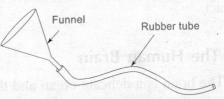

Fig. 9.10 A simple stethoscope

The blood, thus, has the important function of carrying oxygen and nutrients *to* various parts of the body and carrying away the wastes *from* various parts of the body. In addition to this, the blood also maintains body temperature and fights against disease-causing germs. The blood possesses the ability to clot which is important for stopping loss of blood in the case of a wound.

Do You Know?

If all the blood vessels in our body were straightened out and placed end to end, they would be 100,000 miles long; long enough to go around the equator four times.

NERVOUS SYSTEM

The nervous system consists of the brain, the spinal cord, the nerves, and the sense organs. It controls and co-ordinates the various organ systems in higher animals.

You can touch, taste, feel, smell, and hear because of your *sense organs*. Human beings have five sense organs—ear, nose, eyes, skin, and tongue.

Ears are sensitive to sounds and movements. They give us the sense of hearing and help in maintaining balance.

Nose gives us the sense of smell.

Eyes are sensitive to light and enable us to see.

Skin which is sensitive to pressure, heat and cold gives us the sense of touch.

Tongue which is sensitive to chemicals present in food and drinks enables us to taste.

When a sense organ detects a stimulus, it sends messages through the nerves to the brain. The nerves are long cable-like links to and from the brain. They are formed of nerve cells or *neurons* (Fig. 9.11). The brain, in turn, sends messages to the muscles to react.

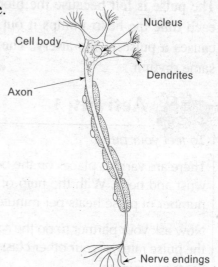

Fig. 9.11 Nerve cell or neuron

The Human Brain

The brain is a delicate organ and the most important organ of the nervous system. It is most developed in humans in comparison to that in any other animal. It is protected by the skull. The brain continues downwards as the spinal cord into our backbone. Different areas of the brain control different functions of the body (Fig. 9.12). Nerves carry messages to the brain from our various sense organs and from the brain to the various muscles. Almost all the actions that we perform are controlled by different parts of the brain except *reflex actions*. These are very fast, involuntary responses to stimuli, and are routed through the spinal cord. For example, we immediately remove our hands when we touch something very hot.

In organisms such as *Paramecium*, *Euglena* and *Amoeba*, the nervous system is absent. Instead they have some other mechanism of coordination between the various parts of the cell.

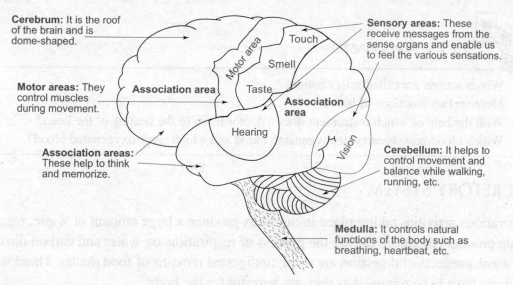

Cerebrum: It is the roof of the brain and is dome-shaped.

Motor areas: They control muscles during movement.

Association areas: These help to think and memorize.

Sensory areas: These receive messages from the sense organs and enable us to feel the various sensations.

Cerebellum: It helps to control movement and balance while walking, running, etc.

Medulla: It controls natural functions of the body such as breathing, heartbeat, etc.

Touch
Motor area
Smell
Association area
Taste
Association area
Hearing
Vision

Fig. 9.12 The human brain showing the different areas associated with different functions

Do You Know?

Each square inch of human skin consists of 19 million cells, 60 hairs, 90 oil glands, 19 feet of blood vessels, 625 sweat glands, and 19,000 sensory cells!

Activity 4

To observe a reflex action.

Sit down and cross your legs such that one leg swings freely. Use the side of your hand to strike the area of your leg just below the knee cap. The leg will jerk forward. The strike was the stimulus and the jerk of the leg was the reflex action.

Reflex actions are not planned earlier. They are spontaneous actions in response to a stimuli. All living organisms, including plants, respond to stimuli.

Recall

- The circulatory system consists of (i) heart (ii) veins (iii) arteries and (iv) capillaries.
- Blood carries nutrients and oxygen to all parts of the body.
- The nervous system is made up of (i) brain (ii) spinal cord (iii) nerves and (iv) sense organs.
- Nerves carry messages or nerve impulses to and from the brain.

Let's Answer

1. Which actions are called reflex actions?
2. Mention two functions of blood.
3. With the help of which instrument does a doctor listen to the beating of the heart?
4. Which blood vessels carry deoxygenated blood and which carry oxygenated blood?

EXCRETORY SYSTEM

The various activities taking place in our body produce a large amount of waste, e.g., the waste products produced during the process of respiration are water and carbon dioxide, the waste products of digestion are solid, undigested remains of food matter. These waste products have to be removed as they are harmful for the body.

In human beings wastes like carbon dioxide are eliminated through the nostrils and mouth; sweat through the sweat glands of the skin; urine through the kidneys and urethra.

Kidneys

Kidneys are one of the most important organs of excretion. The waste materials are filtered out from the blood by the kidneys and eliminated as *urine*. Human beings have a pair of bean-shaped kidneys (Fig. 9.13), each of which gives out a tube called the *ureter*. The two ureters carrying the urine open into a common bladder, the *urinary bladder*. From here the urine is excreted through an opening called the *urethra*.

In lower organisms excretion takes place by the process of diffusion.

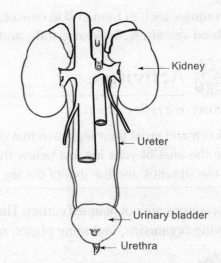

Fig. 9.13   Excretory system in humans

MUSCULAR SYSTEM

The various muscles in our body form the muscular system (Fig. 9.14). They help us in all our activities such as walking, talking, eating, swallowing, etc. Muscles are attached to the skeleton which is made up of a number of bones. They give support to the skeletal system.

There are more than 600 muscles in our body. Muscles can be classified into two groups: *voluntary* and *involuntary* muscles.

Voluntary muscles are those which can be controlled, such as those in your hands and legs.

Involuntary muscles are those that cannot be controlled, such as those in your digestive tract. You may have noticed that you blink your eyelids after every few seconds, but you are not very conscious of it. This is an action that is controlled by involuntary muscles. Contractions of the alimentary canal, urethra, etc., are all involuntary in nature.

Bones and muscles are needed for movement in vertebrates. However, in earthworms, caterpillars, etc., movement takes place by the expansion and contraction of the muscles alone as they have no bones.

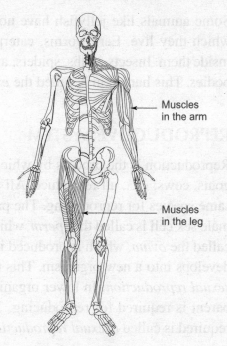

Muscles in the arm

Muscles in the leg

Fig. 9.14   The muscular system in man

SKELETAL SYSTEM

The bones of animals support the different organs of the body and give form and shape to it. They also protect the delicate parts of the body from injury. Bones help us in movement. The different bones are held together by strands of tough tissue called *ligaments*, muscles are attached to bones by *tendons*. The point where two bones are joined together is called a *joint*. Human beings have 206 bones in their bodies doing various functions (Fig. 9.15).

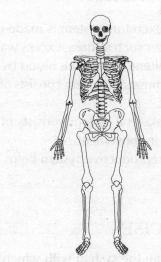

Fig. 9.15   The skeletal system in man

 Do You Know?

Of the 22 bones connected by joints in your skull, only one can move. It is the one in your lower jaw which permits you to talk, laugh and chew food.

Some animals like jellyfish have no skeleton. Their body is supported by the water in which they live. Earthworms, caterpillars have shape but are supported by the liquids inside them. Insects, crabs, spiders, and cockroaches have a hard and tough skin over their bodies. This hard skin is called the *exoskeleton*.

REPRODUCTIVE SYSTEM

Reproduction is the process by which all living things create their own kind. Dogs, cats, goats, cows, etc., all reproduce. All these organisms require a male and a female of the same species for reproducing. The parents have sex organs which produce sex cells. The male sex cell is called the *sperm*, which is produced in the *testes* and the female sex cell is called the *ovum*, which is produced in the *ovaries*. These unite or fuse to form a cell that develops into a new organism. This type of reproduction involving two parents is called *sexual reproduction*. In lower organisms such as *Amoeba*, bacteria, yeast, etc., only one parent is required for reproducing. This type of reproduction where only one parent is required is called *asexual reproduction*.

 Recall

- The excretory system is made up of (i) kidneys (ii) urethra (iii) lungs (iv) skin
- Wastes such as urea, excess water, mineral salts, compounds of calcium and potassium are filtered out of the blood by the kidneys in the form of urine.
- The muscular system consists of voluntary and involuntary muscles which help in movement.
- The skeletal system consists of various bones which give shape to the body and also help in movement.
- The reproductive system helps an organism to create another new organism of its own kind.

EXERCISES

1. **Name the system with which the following organs are associated**
   (a) skin   (b) lungs   (c) liver
   (d) trachea   (e) ribs   (f) brain
   (g) oesophagus   (h) muscles   (i) rectum

2. **Choose the appropriate answer**
   (a) The brain is found within the (ribcage/skull/diaphragm).
   (b) Muscles which move the eyelids are (voluntary/involuntary/both voluntary and involuntary).

(c) Urine is carried from kidneys to the urinary bladder by (urethra/ureters/urea)

(d) The (diaphragm/epiglottis/oesophagus) aids in bringing air in and out of your lungs.

3. **Fill in the blanks**

(a) The waste products of respiration are _____ and _____.

(b) _____ is the process of release of energy.

(c) Two bones move against each other at a _____.

(d) Urine contains urea, numerous salts and _____.

(e) The tube carrying air from the nose to the lungs is _____.

(f) During digestion, food is changed from an insoluble form to a _____ form.

4. **Give one word answers for the following**

(a) Which organ system do the lungs belong to?

(b) Name the hardest substance in the human body.

(c) Which blood vessel causes the pulse beat in your wrist?

(d) Name the organ system and the process which help in the release of energy from blood.

(e) Which muscle present in the chest cavity helps in breathing in and breathing out of air?

(f) What is a fertilized egg called?

(g) Where does the absorption of water take place in the digestive system?

(h) What kind of teeth do herbivorous animals have?

5. **Short answer questions**

(a) Name the different parts of the body system numbered in the figure.

(b) Name the blood vessel of the excretory system.

(c) What does the urinary system do?

(d) What is the function of the kidney?

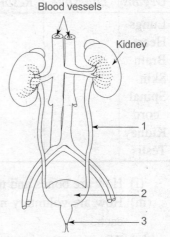

6. **Mark the following sentences as *True* or *False***

(a) Gastric juices are present in the small intestine.

(b) Arteries carry oxygenated blood.

(c) The mouth cavity is a part of the respiratory system.

(d) The reproductive organs are the testes in the male and the ovaries in the female.

(e) Canines are meant for tearing flesh.

(f) Kidney filters the blood.

(g) Brain is an organ of the nervous system.

(h) The urine is expelled from the bladder, from time to time, through a tube called the urethra.

7. **Answer the following questions briefly**

(a) Where are the following located in the human body and what are their functions?

    (i) Heart   (ii) Brain   (iii) Lungs   (iv) Kidney   (v) Spinal cord

(b) (i) Name the important parts of the circulatory system.

    (ii) What is the importance of the circulatory system in our body?

(c) Name the four types of teeth in your mouth. What are their functions?

(d) Draw a diagram of the tongue to show the location of various taste buds.

(e) Explain the difference between arteries, veins and capillaries.

(f) What is a pulse? Why is it felt at a few places only?

(g) What are the main organs of the respiratory system?

(h) What are the functions of blood?

(i) Why do the body cells require oxygen?

(j) Mention the various steps involved in digestion.

(k) Identify and tick the correct organ for the organ systems.

Systems

Organs	Digestive	Respiratory	Circulatory	Nervous	Excretory	Reproductive
Lungs						
Heart						
Brain						
Skin						
Spinal cord						
Kidney						
Testis						

(l) How are bones and muscles interrelated?

(m) How are voluntary muscles different from involuntary muscles? Give an example of each.

(n) What is meant by a reflex action? Give an example.

(o) Explain the mechanism of breathing in of air.

(p) Why do we breathe out more carbon dioxide than oxygen?

(q) (i) Name the various steps of digestion.

    (ii) Name the digestive juice secreted by the liver.

    (iii) Explain the process that takes place in the small intestine.

(r) Give a brief outline of excretion by the kidneys in humans.

(s) Define reproduction. What is meant by sexual reproduction and asexual reproduction?

(t) Sort the following into reflex and voluntary actions:

    (i) reading   (ii) coughing   (iii) writing

(u) Pick the odd one out from the following:
  (i) lungs, kidneys, skin, nose, stomach
  (ii) trachea, brain, lungs, nostrils

THINK AND ANSWER

1. Why should we not breathe in through our mouth?
2. How do the senses of taste and smell protect us from harm?
3. Why is it that the amount of nitrogen breathed in and breathed out remains unchanged?

 Teacher's Notes

- A presentation made in Power Point showing the digestive, respiratory, excretory, and skeletal systems can be shown to the students in the audio-visual room.
- Three-dimensional models of the various organ systems would help the students understand them better.

10

- Rest and motion
- Types of motion—translatory: rectilinear and curvilinear, rotatory, oscillatory
- Speed, displacement and velocity

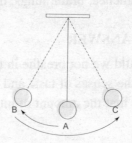

Rest and Motion

REST AND MOTION

All around us we see many objects which are moving. A speeding bus, a boy running down a road, a football rolling along the ground, a bird in flight, and a fruit falling from a tree are all examples of objects in motion. So, what is motion? We can say that objects which are moving, or are showing some movement, are in motion. Similarly, we can say that objects which are not moving are *at rest*.

Ramu sits at the bus stop and looks at a tree across the road. He says that the tree is at rest. Why does he say that? Because, according to Ramu, the position of the tree is not changing with time. Thus,

A body is said to be at rest if it does not change its position with time, with respect to the observer.

Usually a tree on the road, a house, a lamp post on the street corner, etc., would be considered at rest.

Now, while sitting at the bus stop, Ramu sees a bus driving past. He says that the bus is in motion. He says this because the position of the bus is continuously changing with time, with respect to Ramu. Thus,

A body is said to be in motion if its position changes with time, with respect to the observer.

However, no object in the universe can be said to be in a state of absolute rest or absolute motion. The terms *rest* or *motion* are purely relative and are dependent on who the observer is.

This is because a body may be at rest with respect to one observer and at the same time, in motion with respect to another. For example, Ramu sitting at the bus stop sees Mohan driving past him in the bus. So as per Ramu, Mohan is in motion while the tree is at rest. But to Mohan in the bus, the tree on the road appears to be moving backwards. Now if Ramu gets on to the same bus as Mohan, then Ramu would say that Mohan is at rest, while the bus stop and the tree are moving backwards.

The entire universe is in motion

Imagine yourself sitting at your desk or lying in bed. You would certainly consider yourself at rest, at least with respect to the earth. But the earth itself is rotating about its axis, so you are actually in motion along with the earth!

Similarly, you, together with everything else that appears to be at rest on the earth, are *in motion* along with the earth as it makes its journey around the sun. You are in constant motion in relation to the sun and the other heavenly bodies in the universe. In fact, all bodies in the universe are in motion in relation to some other body.

Consider the following examples:

 (a) Radha is standing under a tree and sees her brother running away from her. The distance between Radha and her brother is increasing with time [Fig. 10.1(a)].
 (b) Madan stands at the centre of a circuit racing track and sees a racing car moving along the track [Fig. 10.1(b)]. Madan says that the car is in motion, but the distance between Madan and the car is not changing with time. How would you then justify that the car is in motion in relation to Madan?

(a)   (b)

Fig. 10.1   Examples of motion—change in distance and direction

The position of the car in relation to Madan is changing with time though the distance is not, meaning that the direction of the car in relation to Madan is changing. Thus,

An object is said to be in motion if there is a change in its position or direction with time, with respect to the observer.

Recall

- A body is said to be at rest if it does not change its position with time, with respect to the observer.
- A body is said to be in motion if its position changes with time, in distance or direction, with respect to the observer.
- The terms rest and motion are relative and depend on who the observer is.

Let's Answer

1. Fill in the blanks with the words, *at rest/in motion:*
   (a) The passengers in a running train are _____ in relation to each other but _____ in relation to the signal post at the station.
   (b) A man walking down the aisle of a moving bus is _____ with respect to the bus and _____ with respect to the tree on the road.
   (c) The spokes of the rotating wheel of a bicycle are _____ with respect to each other and _____ with respect to a man standing on the roadside.
   (d) A leaf floating down a stream is _____ with respect to the bank and _____ with respect to the water of the stream.

TYPES OF MOTION

The motion of an object can be of various types (Fig. 10.2).

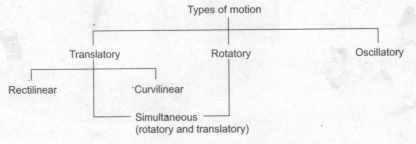

Fig. 10.2 Types of motion

Translatory Motion

Consider the motion of a box sliding down a slope [Fig. 10.3(a)].

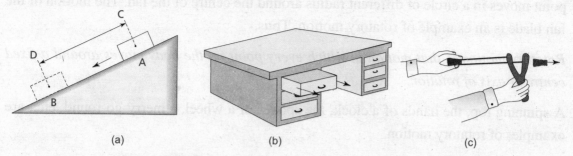

(a)   (b)   (c)

Fig. 10.3   Examples of translatory motion

You will observe that the box as a whole moves from A to B, while the point C on the box moves to the point D. Every point on the box has moved along the same distance CD on the same path. This is an example of an object in translatory motion. Thus,

Translatory motion is that motion in which all points of the body move through the same distance in the same time.

The motion of a drawer of the table, a moving car or train, a box sliding down a slope, a stone flung from a catapult, the motion of a hand while writing, etc., are some other examples of translatory motion (Fig. 10.3).

Let us take the example of the motion of your pen while writing. Sometimes your pen moves in a straight line and sometimes it moves along curves of various shapes.

*When a body moves along a straight line path, it is said to be in **rectilinear motion**.*

*When a body moves along a curved path, it is said to be in **curvilinear motion**.*

Both rectilinear and curvilinear motions are cases of translatory motion, because in both the cases all points on the body are moving along the same path, straight or curved.

Rotatory Motion

Observe the motion of a rotating fan (Fig. 10.4).

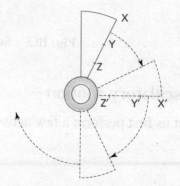

Fig. 10.4   Rotatory motion

You see that point X on the blade of the rotating fan shifts to X′, point Y shifts to Y′, and so on. All points on the blade of the fan do not move along the same path. Instead, each point moves in a circle of different radius around the centre of the fan. The motion of the fan blade is an example of rotatory motion. Thus,

Rotatory motion is that motion in which every point on the body moves around a fixed centre or axis of rotation.

A spinning top, the hands of a clock, the spokes of a wheel, a merry-go-round, etc., are examples of rotatory motion.

Simultaneous Rotatory and Translatory Motion

In some examples, you may feel that both translatory and rotatory motion are occurring simultaneously. For example, the wheel of a bicycle performs rotatory motion about the centre of the wheel as well as translatory motion along the road. The rolling of a ball or the movement of a drill are also examples of this kind. [Fig. 10.5 (a) and (b)]

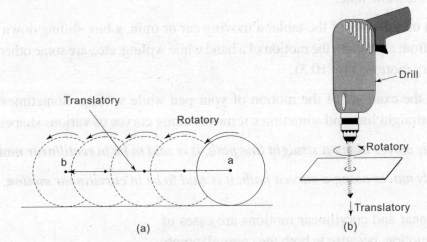

Fig. 10.5 Simultaneous rotatory and translatory motion

Oscillatory Motion

Let us first perform a few activities to demonstrate oscillatory motion.

Activity 1

Materials required A plastic ruler, a table.

Method Take the plastic ruler and hold it at the edge of the table, with a part of the ruler sticking out. Place your hand firmly over the part of the ruler which is on the table to hold it in place. Now with the other hand, pull the extended part of the ruler down a little and release it. What do you observe? (Fig. 10.6).

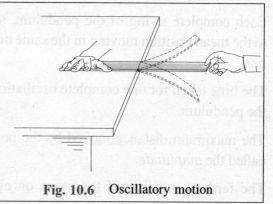

Fig. 10.6 Oscillatory motion

Activity 2

Materials required A piece of thread, stone.

Method Tie a piece of thread to a small stone and suspend it from the edge of the table, as shown in Figure 10.7. Pull the stone gently through a small distance to one side and let go. The stone at first moves back towards the position in which it was when at rest (before you pulled it to one side), then it swings off to the other side of the rest position, goes some distance and stops, then comes back to the rest position and again starts moving in the direction in which you had pulled it. In other words, the stone moves back and forth about the rest position.

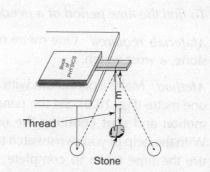

Fig. 10.7 Oscillatory motion

In both these examples, the motion of the extended part of the ruler and the motion of the suspended stone are cases of *oscillatory motion*. Can you state what is common in these two cases? In both the cases, they move to and fro about a fixed position. Thus,

Oscillatory motion is that motion in which a body moves back and forth (or, to and fro) about a fixed position.

A stone suspended with a thread forms what is called a *pendulum* (Fig. 10.8). The position of rest of the

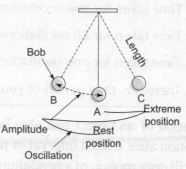

Fig. 10.8 A pendulum

159

stone, i.e., the fixed position about which the pendulum oscillates back and forth, is known as the *mean position*.

Each complete swing of the pendulum, starting from the mean position and returning to the mean position moving in the same direction as in the beginning, is called an *oscillation*.

The time taken for one complete oscillation by the pendulum is called the *time period* of the pendulum.

The maximum distance moved by the pendulum on either side of the mean position is called the *amplitude*.

The farthest position of the stone on either side of the mean position is called the *extreme position*.

Activity 3

To find the time period of a pendulum.

Materials required One metre of thread, a stone, a wrist watch.

Method Make a pendulum with a thread of one metre (Fig. 10.9). Set the pendulum into motion and start counting the oscillations. With the help of your wristwatch try to measure the time taken to complete 10 oscillations, 20 oscillations, and so on. Record you observations as shown:

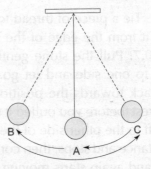

Fig. 10.9 Oscillatory motion of a pendulum

Time taken for 10 oscillations	= _____	s
Time taken for one oscillation	= _____	s
Time taken for 20 oscillations	= _____	s
Time taken for one oscillation	= _____	s
Therefore, time period of your pendulum	= _____	s

Motion of an object can also be *periodic* or *non-periodic*. When an object repeats its motion after a fixed interval of time it is said to be in *periodic motion*. An example is the oscillatory motion of a pendulum. Whereas any motion of any object which is not periodic is said to be *non-periodic*. It may be repetitive but not necessarily happening after fixed intervals of time. For example, the blinking of our eyelids.

Recall

- A body is said to be at rest if it does not change its position with time, with respect to the observer.
- Translatory motion is that motion in which all points of the body move along the same path. If the path is a straight line, the motion is rectilinear, whereas if the path is a curved one, the motion is curvilinear.
- Rotatory motion is that motion in which every point on the body moves around a fixed centre or axis of rotation.
- Oscillatory motion is that motion in which a body moves back and forth (or, to and fro) about a fixed position.

Let's Answer

1. Fill in the blanks.
   (i) An athlete running a hundred metre race along a straight track is executing _____ motion.
   (ii) An athlete running a 1500 m race along the circular track in a stadium is executing _____ motion.

2. In the diagram of an oscillating pendulum (Fig. 10.10), mark the mean position, the extreme positions and the amplitude.

3. Hold one end of a spring in your hand. With the other hand, stretch or compress the other end of the spring and then let go. What kind of a motion do you observe?

4. Identify the following types of motion by marking against each, one of the following identities: R for rectilinear translatory motion, C for curvilinear translatory motion, Ro for rotatory motion, O for oscillatory motion. (You may need to mark more than one identity for some.)
   (i) The motion of a bus along a straight road.
   (ii) The motion of the handle of a bicycle pump.

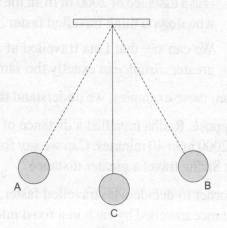

Fig. 10.10   An oscillating pendulum

(iii) The motion of a swing.

(iv) The motion of a screw.

(v) The motion of a plucked sitar string.

(vi) The motion of your hands while skipping.

(vii) The movement of the earth on its axis.

(viii) The motion of a car along the various twists and turns in a crowded lane.

(ix) The motion of the pedal of a bicycle.

(x) The motion of the tip of the minute hand of a clock.

SPEED

You hear the term *speed* in your day-to-day life. Do you know what speed is? Let us take a few examples to understand speed.

(a) Sudha and Radha both started from home at 7.00 a.m. to reach school. Sudha reached school at 7.35 a.m., while Radha reached school at 7.25 a.m. Both Sudha and Radha have travelled an equal distance, but one of them took less time to reach school. So who do you think travelled faster?

We can say that Radha travelled at a faster speed than Sudha, because Radha took less *time* to reach school.

(b) Renu and Lata start from home at the same time and travel by different routes to school. Renu's house is at a distance of 1500 m from the school, while Lata's house is at a distance of 2000 m from the school. Both reach the school at the same time. So, who do you think travelled faster?

We can say that Lata travelled at a faster speed than Renu, because Lata covered a greater *distance* in exactly the same time as Renu.

From these examples, we understand that *speed* depends on both *time* and *distance*.

Suppose, Radha travelled a distance of 1500 m in 20 minutes. Sudha travelled a distance of 2000 m in 40 minutes. Can we say for sure that Sudha travelled slower than Radha? Did not Sudha travel a greater distance?

In order to decide who travelled faster, Radha or Sudha, one would have to compare the distance travelled by each in a fixed interval of time. Assume this fixed interval of time to be 1 minute. Then,

In 1 minute, Radha walked 1500/20 = 75 m, while

In 1 minute, Sudha walked 2000/40   = 50 m

So Radha walked faster than Sudha because Radha travelled a greater distance in 1 minute. Thus,

The speed of a moving body is the distance travelled by it in unit time.

If a moving body travels a distance d in time t, then the speed s is given by

$$s = d/t \qquad (1)$$

Units of Speed

Speed is usually measured in units of km per hour (km/h) or m per second (m/s).

SOLVED EXAMPLES

Example 1   A train covers a distance of 600 km between two towns in 12 hours. What is the speed of the train?

Solution
$$\text{Speed} = \frac{\text{Distance}}{\text{Time}} \quad \therefore \quad \frac{600}{12} = 50 \text{ km/h}$$

Example 2   A bus leaves Guwahati at 8.30 a.m. and reaches Shillong at 11.30 a.m. The speed of the bus is 35 km/h. What is the distance between Guwahati and Shillong?

Solution
$$\text{Distance} = \text{Speed} \times \text{Time} \quad \therefore \quad 35 \times 3 = 105 \text{ km}$$

Example 3   How much time will a car moving at 40 km/h take to travel 360 km?

Solution
$$\text{Time} = \frac{\text{Distance}}{\text{Speed}} = \frac{360}{40} = 9 \text{ h}$$

We can also compare the speeds of two moving bodies by comparing how much time each takes to cover a fixed distance. Suppose, Bus A covers a distance of 500 km in 24 hours. Bus B covers a distance of 600 km in 25 hours. Then Bus A covers 600 km in (24/500) × 600 = 28.8 hours. Bus B covers 600 km in 25 hours.

So, Bus B travels faster than Bus A because it covers the same distance of 600 km in a shorter time.

Example 4 A car travels at 60 km/h. Express the same speed in m/s.

Solution Convert 60 km into m (60 km = 60,000 m)

Convert 1 h into s (1 hour = 60 × 60 sec)

$$\text{Speed} = \frac{60 \times 1000}{3600} = 16.33 \text{ m/s}$$

Example 5 A car travels at 25 m/s. Express the same speed in km/h.

Solution Convert 25 m into km (25 m = 0.025 km)

Convert 1 s into h $\left(1\,\text{s} = \dfrac{1}{60 \times 60}\,\text{h} \right)$

$$\text{Speed} = \frac{25 \times 3600}{1000} = 90 \text{ km/h}$$

Note: Speed in m/s = (Speed in km/h) × $\dfrac{1000}{3600}$

Speed in km/h = (Speed in m/s) × $\dfrac{3600}{1000}$

Uniform and Non-Uniform Motion

A car travels at a constant speed of 50 km/h. In the first hour, it covers 50 km, in the next hour 50 km, and so on. We would then say that the car is in uniform motion.

A body is said to be in uniform motion if it covers equal distances in equal intervals of time.

A cross-country runner starts out with a speed of 8 m/s. After half an hour, he gets tired and his speed slows down to 6 m/s. In the first half-hour, he covers 14.4 km, while in the next half-hour, he covers 10.8 km. We would say that the runner is in non-uniform motion.

A body is said to be in non-uniform motion if it covers unequal distances in equal intervals of time.

- Speed depends on both time and distance.
- Speed is defined as the distance travelled by a moving body in unit time.
- $s = d/t$
- Units of speed are km/h; m/s.
- A body is said to be in uniform motion if it travels equal distances in equal intervals of time.
- A body is said to be in non-uniform motion if it covers unequal distances in equal intervals of time.

Let's Answer

1. Ramesh took 40 minutes to walk to the park 3.2 km away. Sudhir walked to the same park 2 km away from his house in 25 minutes. Who walked faster?

2. Amina cycles 20 km in 2 hours, while Alisha cycles 7 km in half an hour. Who cycles faster? If both started out from the same point at the same time, what would be the distance between both after one hour?

DISPLACEMENT AND VELOCITY

Suppose two cars A and B start out simultaneously from town O. Car A travels towards the north and car B towards the east. After 1 hour, both are at a distance of 40 km from O but their positions with respect to O are not the same. A is 40 km to the north of O and B is 40 km to the east of O (Fig. 10.11).

So, we see that in order to completely specify the position of a moving object with respect to a reference point (in this case O), it is necessary not only to specify the distance of the moving body at any time from O, but also its direction with respect to O.

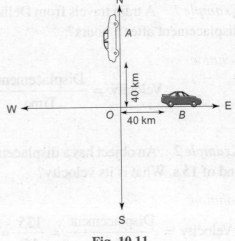

Fig. 10.11

Displacement of a body from a fixed point is its distance from that point in a specified direction (Fig. 10.12).

Similarly, if we say that a car moves with a speed of 40 km/h from *O*, we would not know whether we mean car *A* or car *B*; their motions with respect to *O* are quite different. In order to completely specify the motion of a moving body, it is not enough to state its speed only; we also need to specify the direction in which it is moving.

Velocity of a moving body is its speed in a specified direction, or its rate of change of displacement with time (displacement being with respect to a fixed point) (Fig. 10.13).

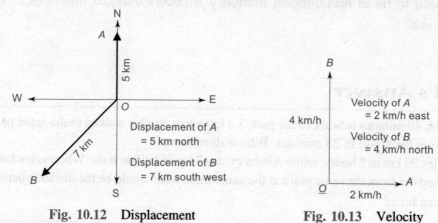

Fig. 10.12   Displacement   **Fig. 10.13   Velocity**

SOLVED EXAMPLES

Example 1   A train travels from Delhi with a velocity of 70 km/h northwards. What is its displacement after 5 hours?

Solution

$$\text{Velocity} = \frac{\text{Displacement}}{\text{Time}} \qquad \therefore \quad \text{Displacement} = \text{Velocity} \times \text{Time}$$
$$= 70 \times 5 = 350 \text{ km north}$$

Example 2   An object has a displacement of 135 m south west of the starting point at the end of 15 s. What is its velocity?

Solution

$$\text{Velocity} = \frac{\text{Displacement}}{\text{Time}} = \frac{135}{15} = 9 \text{ m/s south west}$$

166

Example 3   An object travels with a velocity of 1.5 m/s eastwards for 2 s and then with a velocity of 4 m/s northwards for 1 s. What is its final displacement at the end of 3 s (Fig. 10.14)? (Use the property of right angles.)

Solution   Displacement along *OA*

$$= \text{Velocity} \times \text{Time} = 1.5 \text{ m} \times 2 = 3 \text{ m}$$

Displacement along *AB*

$$= \text{Velocity} \times \text{Time} = 4 \text{ m} \times 1 = 4 \text{ m}$$

Final displacement at the end of 3 s (*OB*)

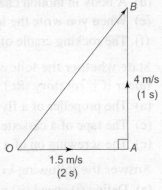

Fig. 10.14

$$OB = \sqrt{OA^2 + AB^2} = \sqrt{3^2 + 4^2} = \sqrt{9 + 16} = \sqrt{25} = 5 \text{ m in the direction } OB.$$

 Recall

- Displacement of a body from a fixed point is its distance from that point in a specified direction.
- Velocity of a moving body is its rate of change of displacement with time.

 Let's Answer

1. How is (a) displacement different from distance (b) speed different from velocity?
2. A boy travels a distance of 3 km in the northwest direction, in 1 minute. What is his velocity (in m/s)?   (50 m/s, NW)
3. Sunita drives at 40 km per hour eastwards for 30 minutes. What is her displacement at the end of the drive?   (20 m, E)
4. Vanita travels due north at 3 m/s for 2 s and then due east at 8 m/s for 1 s. What is her final displacement with respect to her starting position? Show your answer with a diagram. (10 m)

EXERCISES

1. **Mark the following sentences as *True* or *False***
    (a) A man sitting in a moving train is in motion in relation to a passenger sitting on the next seat.
    (b) A passenger in a flying aeroplane is at rest with respect to the airport.
    (c) A body can be at rest and in motion at the same time with respect to the same observer.

(d) A body in motion changes its distance or direction in relation to a given observer.

(e) When you write the letter "O", your pen performs rectilinear translatory motion.

(f) The rocking cradle of a baby is an example of oscillatory motion.

2. State whether the following motions are translatory rectilinear (R), translatory curvilinear (C), rotatory (Ro), or oscillatory (O)

(a) The propeller of a flying helicopter.

(b) A bullet fired from a gun.

(c) The tape of a cassette recorder.

(d) The hour hand of a watch.

(e) The screwing on of a bottle cap.

(f) The plucked string of a guitar.

3. Answer the following in one word or sentence

(a) Define (i) speed (ii) velocity (iii) displacement.

(b) Write the units of the following physical quantities: (i) speed (ii) velocity.

(c) Classify the following motions as uniform and non-uniform:

    (i) A train runs from New Delhi to Calcutta. It covers a distance of 500 km in 8 hours and a distance of 750 km also in 8 hours.

    (ii) Madhu takes part in a car race. She drives a distance of 80 km in the first, second and third hours.

4. Answer the following questions briefly

(a) Define the terms amplitude and time period for a pendulum.

(b) Explain curvilinear and rotatory motions, giving examples to show the difference between them.

Numerical Problems

1. Convert the following speeds into m/s:

    (a) 36 km/h   (b) 45 km/h

2. Convert the following speeds into km/h:

    (a) 25 m/s   (b) 15 m/s

3. What distance would a car travelling at a constant speed of 60 m/s cover in 5 s?

4. Sushil cycles 500 m in 50 s. How long will it take him to cycle 1.5 km, if he cycles at this constant speed?

5. In the table given below, we see the motion of two bodies A and B. Each dot represents the position of the body after 1/5 s. In what motion are the bodies A and B? Fill in the positions of the bodies A and B for the next 4 intervals of 1/5 s:

	Position of the body after every 1/5 seconds									
Motion A →	0 m	0.5 m	1.0 m	1.5 m	2.0 m	2.5 m	—	—	—	—
B →	0 m	0.5 m	1.10 m	1.80 m	2.60 m	3.50 m	—	—	—	—

Answers

1. (a) 10 m/s   (b) 12.5 m/s   2. (a) 90 km/h   (b) 54 km/h
3. 300 m   4. 150 s
5. A is in uniform motion, B is in non-uniform motion.
   $A \rightarrow$ 3.0 m; 3.5 m; 4 m; 4.5 m
   $B \rightarrow$ 4.5 m; 5.6 m; 6.8 m, 8.1 m

THINK AND ANSWER

Elaborate with examples the distinction between
 (a) distance and displacement
 (b) speed and velocity
 (c) uniform and non-uniform velocity

Teacher's Notes

- Concepts of distance and displacement; speed and velocity may be elaborated with more examples.

11

- Force and effects of force
- Types of forces
- Friction—causes, effects and ways of reducing it
- Pressure and fluid pressure

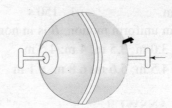

Force and Pressure

FORCE

A ball is lying at rest on the ground. You want to make the ball move towards your friend. What would you do? You could force the ball to move by kicking it towards your friend.

Suppose the ball is moving towards you through the air. You could force it to stop by catching it with your hand.

A car is travelling on a road with very little traffic. By pressing on the accelerator, the driver of the car can force the car to move faster.

Imagine the same car coming down a flyover dangerously fast. The driver can apply the brakes to force the car to slow down.

You are packing your bag for school, and have difficulty in taking one more notebook as the bag is too full. You could force the last notebook into the bag but in the process the notebook may get bent, i.e., its shape may change.

In all these examples the word force is commonly used. What do we understand by the term *force*? These examples also give you an idea of some of the things that force can do. Thus,

A force is that agency which can change the state of rest or motion of a body.

EFFECTS OF FORCE

From the examples discussed above we can infer that force can make the following happen:

- Force can set a body at rest into motion.
- It can bring a body in motion to rest.
- It can change the direction of motion of a body.
- It can make a moving object move faster.
- It can make a moving object move slower.
- It can change the shape of an object.

Force is measured in terms of a unit called *newton* (abbreviated as N).

Now identify the force and the effect of the force in each of the following actions.

The first one is done for you.

Actions	Force	Effect of force
(a) Child pulling along a toy	Child pulling forwards	Toy at rest is set into motion
(b) Girl pulling back a dog, on a leash, to stop him		
(c) Child pushing another child on swing		
(d) Pair of hands rolling a chapati		
(e) Children pedalling their bicycles and moving faster		
(f) Stretching a spring		

More than One Force on a Body

In Figure 11.1(a), Kamal is pushing a heavy crate with a force of 50 N. Now if Nirmal also joins him and pushes the crate in the same direction with another force of 50 N, then it is easier to move the crate. Why is this so? What is the total force acting on the crate when both Kamal and Nirmal push it as shown in Figure 11.1(a).

The total force on the crate is the force applied by Kamal plus the force applied by Nirmal, i.e., 50 N + 50 N = 100 N.

Now let us look at Figure 11.1(b). If Kamal continues to push the crate in the same way while Vimal pulls it with the rope in the same direction from the other side, then too, the total force on the crate will be 50 N + 50 N = 100 N.

If Kamal and Nirmal start applying their forces to the crate as shown in Figure 11.2(a), what do you think will happen? What will be the total force on the crate?

Now look at Figure 11.2(b). If Kamal pushes with a greater force than Nirmal, then what do you think will happen to the crate? What is the total force acting on the crate in this case?

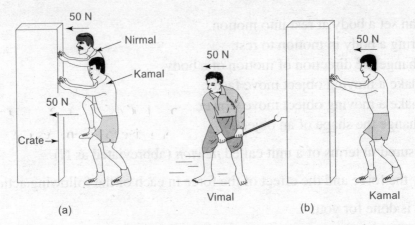

Fig. 11.1   Effect of more than one force acting on a body

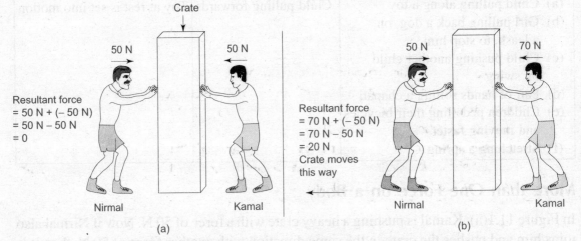

Fig. 11.2   Resultant force — two forces acting on a body simultaneously

Thus,

If two or more than two forces act on a body simultaneously, then the total force acting on the body is called the resultant force.

The resultant force determines how easily and in what direction the body will move.

- When two forces act on a body in the same direction, the resultant force is found by *adding* the two forces and it makes the body move in the same direction as the two forces.

- When two forces act on a body in opposite directions, the resultant force is found by the *difference* of the two forces and it makes the body move in the direction of the larger force.
- If two *equal* forces act on the body in *opposite directions*, then the resultant force on the body will be zero and the body will not move.

Recall

- A force can change the state of rest on motion of a body, or change its shape.
- If two or more forces act on a body, the total or effective force on the body is called the resultant force.

Let's Answer

1. In the situations given here, determine the resultant force and the direction in which the body will move:
   (a) Two horses pull a cart in the forward direction, each with a force of 2000 N.
   (b) A tow truck pulls a car forward with a force of 1200 N, while a second car pushes the first car forward from behind with a force of 500 N.
   (c) Twins, Prema and Padma, had a fight over a doll. Prema pulled the doll's left hand towards herself with a force of 40 N, while Padma pulled the doll's right hand in the opposite direction with a force of 40 N.
   (d) In a tug-of-war, children of team A pull the rope towards themselves with forces of 120 N, 100 N and 150 N. Students of team B pull the rope in the opposite direction with forces of 130 N, 120 N and 150 N.

TYPES OF FORCES

In our daily life we come across many different types of forces. For example, we use the muscular force of our muscles to lift a bucket of water. Let us study the different types of forces found around us.

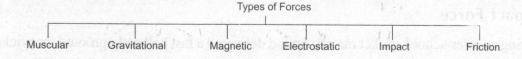

Types of Forces

| Muscular | Gravitational | Magnetic | Electrostatic | Impact | Friction |

Muscular Force

Rajesh played football all Sunday morning. Then he felt very tired as he had exercised his muscles a lot. Sunita and her friends went for a long, strenuous trek. At the end of it, her muscles ached. In walking, running, kicking, etc., you are using your muscles.

The force applied by the muscles of the body is called muscular force.

Bullocks, mules, horses, etc., use their muscular force to do work.

Gravitational Force

A ball thrown upwards always comes down. A ripe fruit from a tree always falls straight down. If you want to hold up your book in the air, you have to make an effort to do so, otherwise it will come down to the ground. This is because of the gravitational force.

The force with which the earth pulls all objects towards itself is called the gravitational force.

The gravitational force acting on a body is also called its *weight*. The weight of a body of mass 1 kg is called a kilogram weight and is equal to 9.8 newton.

Magnetic Force

Many of you must have played with magnets. A magnet attracts iron nails, pins, etc. It also attracts or repels other magnets.

Forces associated with magnets are known as magnetic forces.

Electrostatic Force

When you comb your hair vigorously with a dry plastic comb on a winter morning, you will find that the comb starts attracting small pieces of paper. This is because the comb has become electrically charged.

Forces associated with electrically charged bodies are known as electrostatic forces.

Impact Force

During an inter-school cricket match, Anand delivered a fast ball and uprooted the wicket. Here, the impact of the fast-moving ball succeeded in uprooting the wicket. When you hold the tip of a nail on a wooden object and strike the head of the nail with a hammer, the impact of the hammer makes the nail go into the wood.

A force produced by the impact of one body on another is called an impact force.

Friction

Suraj tried to roll a ball on the rough floor of the courtyard outside his house. The ball stopped after moving through a small distance. However, when he tried to roll the ball on the smooth floor of his room, the ball travelled a much longer distance before coming to a stop. The ball stops rolling on the floor due to a force between the ball and the floor which tries to oppose the motion of the ball on the floor. This force is known as *friction*; it is large between two rough surfaces and less between two smooth surfaces.

The force acting between a pair of surfaces in contact and tending to oppose the motion of one surface over the other is called the force of friction.

 Recall

- Force is an agent which can change the state of rest or motion of a body.
- A force can set a body into motion, bring it to rest, change its direction of motion, make it move faster or slower, and change its shape.
- If two forces act in the same direction, the resultant force is the sum of the two forces.
- If two forces act in opposite directions, the resultant force is the difference of the two forces.
- If two equal forces act in opposite directions, the resultant force is zero.
- Some of the common types of forces are muscular force, gravitational force, magnetic force, electrostatic force, impact force, and frictional force.

 Let's Answer

1. In each of the pictures given here, identify the type of force that is acting in each of the situations:

(Contd...)

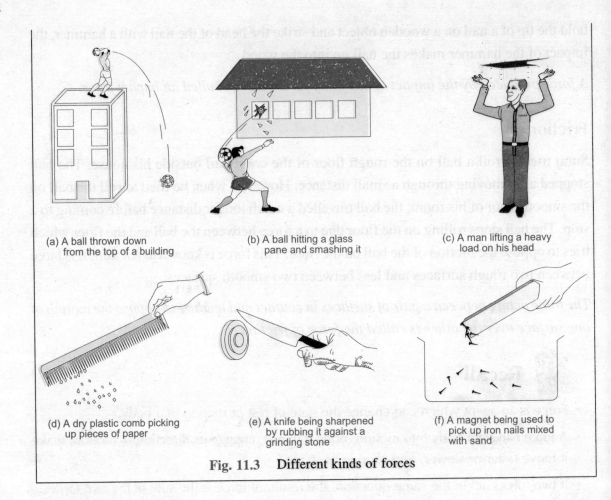

(a) A ball thrown down from the top of a building

(b) A ball hitting a glass pane and smashing it

(c) A man lifting a heavy load on his head

(d) A dry plastic comb picking up pieces of paper

(e) A knife being sharpened by rubbing it against a grinding stone

(f) A magnet being used to pick up iron nails mixed with sand

Fig. 11.3   Different kinds of forces

FRICTION

You have already seen that the force of friction

- acts between a pair of surfaces in contact,
- tends to prevent the motion of one surface over the other, and
- is less between smooth surfaces and greater between rough surfaces.

What Causes Friction?

Have you seen the saw used by a carpenter? When the teeth of two such saws get inter-locked, it becomes very difficult to move one over the other (Fig. 11.4). We have a similar situation when we try to move one surface over another. Although a surface may appear to be smooth when seen with the naked eye, under a microscope we would observe many irregularities (Fig. 11.5). These surface irregularities get interlocked like the teeth of the saw and make the motion of one surface over the other difficult. The more the irregularities, i.e., rougher the surface, the greater the opposition to the motion of one surface over the other, and hence greater is the force of friction.

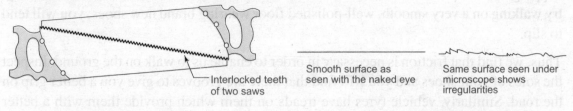

Fig. 11.4   Friction   Fig. 11.5   Surface irregularities

Interlocked teeth of two saws

Smooth surface as seen with the naked eye

Same surface seen under microscope shows irregularities

EFFECTS OF FRICTION

On a cold day when you rub your hands together, you feel warm. The friction between your hands produces heat. Early man discovered fire by rubbing together two pieces of stone called *flint*. The heat produced by friction between the stones gave rise to a spark that led to the discovery of fire. Thus, *friction produces heat*.

The tyres of a car get worn out with time. Do you notice any difference between the soles of a new pair of shoes and those of an older pair? The lead of your pencil gets blunt as you keep writing. Parts of machines that keep on rubbing against each other get worn out due to friction between them. Thus, *friction causes wear and tear of the surfaces in contact*.

How do we Reduce Friction?

One way to reduce friction is to make the surfaces in contact smoother. Take a little oil on the palm of your hand and then rub the palms of your hands together. You will feel them sliding over each other more easily. Thus, oil or grease make the surface smoother and reduce friction. That is why, the moving parts of machines are also covered with oil or grease to reduce friction between them and decrease their wear and tear. Substances like oil or grease which are used to reduce friction are called *lubricants*.

Another way to reduce friction is to *use wheels or rollers*. You may have seen that some suitcases are provided with wheels. Try moving the same suitcase over the floor by dragging it by the surface that does not have wheels. Then try moving it by the wheeled surface. You will feel that it is much easier to move it over the wheels. When heavy objects have to be moved from one place to another, rollers are used to make the movement easier. Similarly, tiny steel balls called *ball bearings* are often placed between moving parts of machines to reduce friction and make their movement easier.

SIGNIFICANCE OF FRICTION

Try to walk over a floor on which soap water has been spilt and you will find yourself slipping. The soap water has reduced the friction between your feet and the floor. Similarly, try walking on a very smooth, well-polished floor wearing brand new shoes; you will tend to slip.

Thus, we find that friction is necessary in order to enable us to walk on the ground. Inspect the soles of your shoes and you will find that there are grooves to give you a better grip on the road. Similarly, vehicle tyres have treads on them which provide them with a better grip on the road and prevent their skidding on wet road surfaces.

Why is it difficult to unscrew a bottle cap with wet or oily hands? If you strike a match on the smooth, worn out surface of an old, used match box, will you be able to light the match?

Friction is often said to be a necessary evil. Though friction causes a lot of trouble for us yet we cannot imagine our lives without friction.

Recall

- Friction produces heat and causes wear and tear.
- Friction can be reduced with the help of lubricants or by providing wheels or rollers.
- Friction is a necessary evil. It helps us in many ways.

Let's Answer

1. Suggest a way by which you reduce friction between the carrom board and the striker and coins.
2. Why does a piece of chalk get smaller as the teacher writes with it on the blackboard.
3. Give one example where friction is (a) desirable (b) undesirable.

PRESSURE

Press down the palm of your left hand with the thumb of the right hand [Fig. 11.6(a)]. Next hold a pin vertically between the thumb and the palm and press the palm [Fig. 11.6(b)].

What do you feel? You feel a sharp jab of pain, much more than when you pressed only with the thumb. This is because

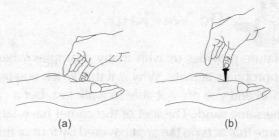

(a)   (b)

Fig. 11.6 Pressure

- in the first case, the force of the thumb of the right hand was spread out evenly over a much larger area, i.e., the area of the thumb.
- in the second case, the force acts on a very small area, namely the tip of the pin, so you feel the effect of the force much more.

Thus, the effect of a force depends on the area over which it acts.

Pressure is defined as the force acting per unit area.

To calculate pressure, we divide the total force by the total area over which it acts:

$$\text{Pressure} = \frac{\text{Force}}{\text{Area}} \qquad (2)$$

Units of Pressure

The units of pressure are N/m^2 or N/cm^2 (newton per square metre or newton per square centimetre) or kg wt/m^2 or kg wt/cm^2 (kilogram weight per square metre or per square centimetre).

SOLVED EXAMPLES

Example 1   A force of 20 N acts over an area of 5 cm^2. What is the pressure?

Solution   From Equation (2),

$$\text{Pressure} = \frac{\text{Force}}{\text{Area}}; \quad \text{Force} = 20 \text{ N}; \text{Area} = 5 \text{ cm}^2$$

$$\text{Pressure} = \frac{20}{5} = 4 \text{ N/cm}^2$$

Example 2   A pressure of 25 N/m^2 acts on an area of 4 m^2. Calculate the total force?

Solution

$$\text{Pressure} = \frac{\text{Force}}{\text{Area}}; \quad 25 = \frac{\text{Force}}{4}$$

$$\text{Total Force} = 25 \times 4 = 100 \text{ N}$$

179

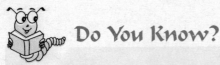
Nature provides us with many examples where the right kind of pressure is used for the appropriate activity. Why is it that when you try to walk on soft sand, your feet sink into the sand and you are not able to walk fast, but a camel is able to walk quite fast and easily on the same sand? The feet of the camel have large flat pads. The weight of the camel is the force that acts on the area covered by four of these large padded feet. Since the feet have a large area, the pressure is much less and so the feet do not sink in.

A woodpecker has a long, hard, sharp, and pointed beak. It hammers with its beak at the wood and can scoop out the wood and make a hole in the tree as it wants. How does the pointed beak help it? The tip of the beak being a point, the area covered by it is very small, so the pressure is very high for any force that the woodpecker applies, high enough to cut through the wood! (Fig. 11.7)

Fig. 11.7   A woodpecker

 Recall

- Pressure is the force acting per unit area.

- Pressure = $\dfrac{\text{Force}}{\text{Area}}$

- Units of pressure are N/m² or N/cm²; kg wt/m² or kg wt/cm².

 Let's Answer

1. What are the S.I. units of pressure?
2. If a force of 10 N acts on an area of 1 cm², what is the pressure?   (10 N/cm²)
3. What force would produce the same pressure on a surface of area 4 cm²?   (40 N)
4. How do the broad feet of camels help them to walk on sand?

Atmospheric Pressure

The earth, we know, is surrounded by the atmosphere. It extends up to a height of a few hundred kilometres above the earth's surface. This air has weight. At sea level, every litre of air weighs about 1.3 g wt. All objects on the earth's surface therefore experience the pressure due to this force. This pressure is called *atmospheric pressure* (Fig. 11.8).

The weight of the atmosphere on each square cm on the earth's surface is approximately 1 kg wt.

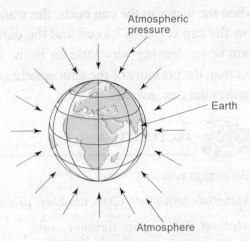

Fig. 11.8 A diagram demonstrating atmospheric pressure

Hold your palm and roughly estimate its area. Let us say that this area is nearly 60 sq cm. Then the weight of the atmosphere on your hand is *nearly 60 kg wt*. If you try to calculate the weight of the atmosphere on top of your head in this manner, you would find that it is about 250 kg wt, i.e., about the weight of two small elephants.

Effects of Atmospheric Pressure

Let us try the following activities to observe the effects of atmospheric pressure.

Activity 1

Crushing can experiment

Materials required Empty tin can, water, burner.

Method Take an empty tin can and fill half of it with water. Heat the can till the water boils and the water vapour drives off the air above the water in the can. Quickly close the mouth of the can with an airtight cap and cool the can under a tap. What happens to the can? (Fig. 11.9)

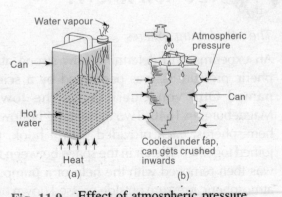

Fig. 11.9 Effect of atmospheric pressure

When the water in the can boils, the water vapour displaces most of the air in the can. If now the cap is tightly closed and the can cooled quickly, the water vapour condenses to form water, leaving very little air in the can. This air has a pressure that is considerably less than the pressure of the atmosphere outside; hence, the external atmospheric pressure crushes the can inwards.

Activity 2

Defying gravity

Materials required Glass tumbler, piece of cardboard, water.

Method Fill a glass tumbler completely with water right up to the brim. Now very carefully slide a piece of card board over the top of the glass covering the mouth of the glass. Hold the card down over the mouth of the tumbler and then turn the tumbler upside down. Now remove your hand from the card. You will find that the card remains stuck to the mouth of the tumbler and the water does not fall down! (Fig. 11.10). Can you explain why?

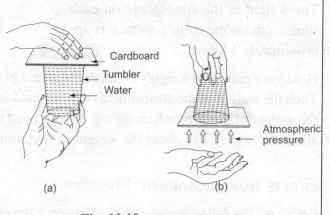

Fig. 11.10 Defying gravity

Do You Know?

The Magdeburg spheres

An experiment to determine how strong atmospheric pressure is, was performed by a scientist named Otto von Guericke, in the town of Magdeburg, in 1640. Two tight-fitting hollow iron hemispheres, each provided with a hook, were joined together. The air in the space between them was then removed with the help of a pump. The atmospheric pressure outside pressed down on the hemispheres. So great was this pressure that it required two teams of eight horses, each pulling in opposite directions, to separate the two hemispheres (Fig. 11.11).

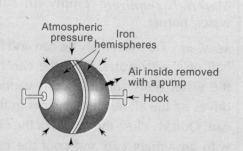

Fig. 11.11 Magdeburg spheres

Measuring Atmospheric Pressure

Atmospheric pressure is measured using an instrument called the *barometer*. The first barometer was made by an Italian scientist, Evangelista Torricelli.

Construction of a Mercury Barometer

You too can follow the same steps that Torricelli did and make your own barometer.

Take a narrow glass tube about 80 cm long and closed at one end. Fill it up with mercury up to the brim and seal it with your finger [Fig. 11.12 (a)]. Invert the tube and with your finger still in place, dip the sealed end into a trough containing mercury [Fig. 11.12 (b)].

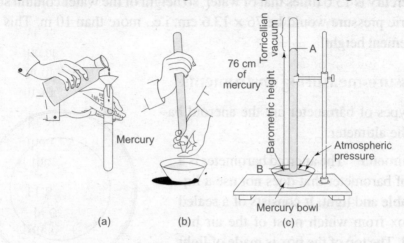

Fig. 11.12   Construction of a mercury barometer

Now remove your finger. You will notice that some of the mercury in the tube flows into the trough, leaving an empty space at the closed end of the tube. But an appreciable amount of mercury remains standing in the tube. If you measure the height of the mercury with a metre scale, you will find that it is approximately 76 cm [Fig. 11.12 (c)].

Atmospheric pressure acts on the surface of the mercury in the trough (since this surface is exposed to the atmosphere). This atmospheric pressure is capable of supporting the height of the mercury that remains in the tube (i.e., 76 cm). This height of 76 cm of mercury at sea level is taken as a measure of the atmospheric pressure. If you take your barometer up to a high mountain where the atmospheric pressure is lower, you will find that the height of the mercury in the tube will fall, corresponding to the atmospheric pressure at that place.

The pressure that can balance a 76 cm high column of mercury is said to be one atmosphere.

$$1 \text{ atmosphere} = 76 \text{ cm of mercury} = 1033 \text{ g wt/cm}^2 = 1033 \text{ cm of water}$$

What do you think the space above the mercury in the glass tube contains? Initially it contained mercury because you had filled up the whole tube with mercury. Now when the mercury has flowed out of it, it does not contain air, since the top of the tube is closed. So... it contains nothing! This space is said to be a *vacuum*.

If you made a barometer using water instead of mercury, what height of water would be supported by the atmospheric pressure?

Density of mercury is 13.6 times that of water, so height of the water column supported by the atmospheric pressure would be 76×13.6 cm, i.e., more than 10 m. This would be a rather inconvenient height!

Other Pressure-measuring Instruments

Some other types of barometer are the aneroid barometer and the altimeter.

Aneroid barometer   The aneroid barometer is a special kind of barometer that does not use a liquid. It is portable and light. It consists of a sealed light metal box from which most of the air has been removed. The top of the box is made of light foil which is very sensitive to slight changes in the atmospheric pressure. These changes are recorded by a system of levers which makes a pointer move on a scale (Fig. 11.13).

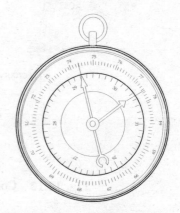

Fig. 11.13   Aneroid barometer

Altimeter   In aircrafts we use a special kind of aneroid barometer called the *altimeter*. This is used to measure the height at which the aircraft is flying based on the change in atmospheric pressure (Fig. 11.14).

Remember: The atmospheric pressure *decreases* with height.

Fig. 11.14   Altimeter

Uses of a barometer

A barometer is used to

1. measure the atmospheric pressure.
2. forecast weather conditions.
3. measure the height of a place above sea level.

 Do You Know?

How does the atmospheric pressure affect our bodies?

You may certainly wonder that if the atmospheric pressure is so great, then why are our bodies not crushed under it? This does not happen because the bodies of humans and other living organisms are made up of cells which have fluids that exert from within a pressure equal to the atmospheric pressure. Thus, the two pressures balance each other.

However, under certain circumstances, this balance gets upset. If you have ever gone trekking to high altitudes where the atmospheric pressure is lower than at sea level, you will find that the pressure of the fluids inside the body becomes greater in comparison causing some blood vessels to burst. Thus, nose bleeding is frequently observed in high altitude climbers.

Astronauts wear specially made suits to go into space where the external pressure is much lower than the normal atmospheric pressure. These suits maintain a pressure equal to the atmospheric pressure in the space between the suit and the body. This arrangement makes sure that the body cells do not burst under the high internal pressure.

 Recall

- The layer of air surrounding the earth is called the atmosphere.

- The pressure exerted by the atmosphere on the earth is called atmospheric pressure.

- Atmospheric pressure is measured using a barometer.

- A pressure that can balance a 76 cm high column of mercury is said to be one atmosphere.

- The atmospheric pressure decreases with height.

- The aneroid barometer is a portable form of the barometer.

- The altimeter helps us to find the height of a place above sea level.

- The barometer is used to (a) measure atmospheric pressure and height (b) forecast weather conditions.

Let's Answer

1. How does the atmospheric pressure vary with height above the earth?
2. Give three uses of a barometer.
3. Which kind of barometer would you prefer to use to measure the pressure inside an aircraft, a mercury barometer or an aneroid barometer?
4. Why do we often have a nose-bleed when we climb up to higher altitudes?

PRESSURE IN FLUIDS

Liquids and gases flow and do not have a definite shape, unlike solids. Hence, liquids and gases are called *fluids*.

You have already seen how air in the atmosphere around us exerts pressure. In fact, all liquids and gases, i.e., fluids exert pressure.

Activity 3

To show that pressure varies with height.

Materials required A glass tube, balloon, rubber band.

Method Take a glass tube about 10 cm long and 3 cm wide. Cut out a piece of rubber membrane from a balloon and tie it with a rubber band around one end of the glass tube as shown in Figure 11.15. Now holding the tube vertical, pour some water into it from the other end.

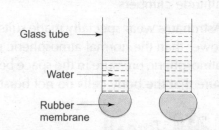

Fig. 11.15 Pressure increases with increase in height

The membrane bulges out due to the pressure of the water in it. Now pour some more water into the tube and observe what happens to the bulge of the membrane. The bulge of the membrane increases showing that the *pressure exerted by the liquid increases with increase in the height of the liquid.*

Activity 3

To make a pressure-measuring instrument.

Materials required A U tube, rubber tube, funnel, rubber membrane, rubber band, vessel of water, mercury.

Method Take some mercury in a U tube. Connect one end of the U tube by a piece of rubber tubing to the long end of a funnel as shown in Figure 11.16. Make sure to hold the U tube vertical, so that mercury does not spill out. Close the wide mouth of the funnel with a stretched piece of rubber membrane, tie it with a rubber band. Note that the height of mercury in both limbs of the U tube is equal.

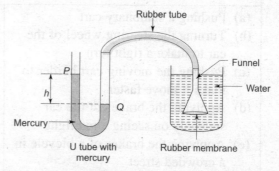

Fig 11.16 Instrument for measuring pressure

Now push the funnel into a vessel of water. As you push the funnel down further into the water, you will observe that the level of mercury in *Q* goes below the level in *P*. The pressure of the water is transmitted via the rubber membrane to the air in the funnel and the rubber tube, which then exerts pressure on the mercury in *Q*. The difference in heights of mercury in *P* and *Q*—*h*—becomes a measure of the pressure of the water. This instrument is called a *manometer*. Observe what happens to *h* as you push the funnel deeper into the water.

Now turn the mouth of the funnel around in all directions, including upwards, *at the same level in the water.* What happens to *h*?

In the first case h increases indicating that *pressure increases with depth below the free surface of the liquid.*

In the second case *h* does not show any change. This tells us that *a liquid exerts uniform pressure in all directions, at a particular height within the liquid.* These properties are true for all fluids in general which are enclosed in a vessel.

 Recall

- Pressure due to a liquid increases with depth below the free surface of the liquid.
- A liquid exerts uniform pressure in all directions, at a particular height within the liquid.

EXERCISES

1. **Mark the following sentences as *True* or *False***
   (a) A boy doing push-ups is applying electrostatic force.
   (b) It is easier to run on a wet floor than on a dry one because friction is less on a wet floor.

2. Match the following columns

Column 1	Column 2
(a) Pushing a stationary cart	(i) Force changing the direction of motion
(b) Turning the steering wheel of the car to make a right turn	(ii) Force causing a body to move slower
(c) Pushing the moving cart harder to make it move faster	(iii) Force causing a body to stop
(d) Applying the brakes of the car suddenly on seeing a red light	(iv) Force causing a body to start moving
(e) Applying the brakes of a bicycle in a crowded street	(v) Force causing a body to move faster

3. Answer in one or two sentences

(a) What instruments are used for measuring atmospheric pressure?

(b) Give the uses of a barometer.

(c) What is one atmosphere?

4. Give reasons for the following

(a) When you place a straw in a bottle of cold drink and suck at the end of the straw, the liquid rises up in the straw to your mouth.

(b) A doctor pushes down the plunger of the syringe, places its nozzle in the medicine and then pulls up the plunger to make the medicine rise up in the syringe.

(c) Ravi puts the end of a dropper into the ink, squeezes the rubber bulb and then releases it. The ink rises up in the dropper.

(d) Charu fractured his arm and had to have a heavy plaster put around it. The doctor put his plastered arm in a sling made of á thin strip of gauze. Charu found it very difficult to carry his arm in that sling. So his mother made a sling out of a wide dupatta and with this Charu found it much easier to carry his arm.

(e) Rahul and Usha were fighting. When Rahul hit Usha with the edge of the ruler, it was much more painful for Usha than when he hit her with the flat side of the ruler.

(f) When you wear high-heeled shoes, you exert less pressure on the ground than when you wear flat shoes.

(g) A barometer on top of Mt. Everest will record less than 76 cm of mercury.

5. Answer the following questions briefly

(a) What effect of a force is demonstrated by the following?

   (i) When a rubber band is pulled—it stretches.

   (ii) When a cricketer uses his bat to deflect an oncoming ball towards the boundary.

   (iii) Sudha pushes the swing of her little sister, who is already swinging, to make the swing move higher.

(b) What is a force? Give examples to show how a force may be used to (i) change the direction of a body (ii) alter the shape of a body.

(c) What types of forces are involved in each of the following situations:

   (i) Arun throws a stone to hit a mango on a tree and the mango falls down.

   (ii) Shiela pedals her bicycle using her legs. The wheels of the bicycle rub along the road as the cycle moves on.

(d) Explain, why?

   (i) An eraser gets smaller and smaller as you use it.

   (ii) Sparks are produced when a knife is sharpened against a grinding wheel.

   (iii) You will slip and fall if you try to walk on a surface over which oil has been spilt.

   (iv) Luggage trolleys are provided with wheels.

   (v) The leather soles of a new pair of shoes are rubbed with sandpaper.

   (vi) A car having worn out tyres is more likely to skid on a rainy day.

   (vii) How do we measure atmospheric pressure? Explain in detail the construction of a mercury barometer. Support your answer with diagrams.

Numerical Problems

1. The pressure on a surface of 25 m^2 is 7 N/m^2. What is the total force acting on the body?
2. A force of 800 N exerts a pressure of 16 N/cm^2. What is the area on which the force acts?
3. A force of 1800 N acts on the surface of a rectangular block of length 6 m and breadth 4 m. What is the pressure?

Answers

   1. 175 N   2. 50 cm^2 3. 75 N/m^2

THINK AND ANSWER

1. A horse pulls a cart with a force of 1700 N. The force of friction between the cart and the ground is 500 N. What is the resultant force of the cart?
2. Write an account of ten events involving forces that occurred around you today, stating the kind of force involved in each, and the effect of the force in that event.
3. Why are dams broader at the base than at the top?

Teacher's Notes

- Emphasize on day-to-day examples involving different effects of forces.
- Examples of uniform and non-uniform motion may be used extensively, relating non-uniform motion to the existence of a force.

12

- Levers
- Pulleys
- The inclined plane
- The screw
- The wheel

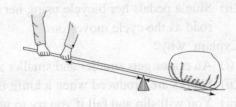

Simple Machines

Have you ever been to the construction site of a building? Today, we find that multi-storeyed buildings are constructed in just a few months. Various kinds of machines are used for the work, some of which are quite complicated. In reality, however, most of these machines are a combination of certain simple machines which help you to do the work faster and with less effort. In this chapter, we shall look at some of these simple machines and understand how they help us.

Do You Know?

The Taj Mahal in Agra is one of the most beautiful pieces of architecture that the world has known. This magnificent structure soars to a height of 60 m and stands on an area of 580 m × 304 m. Its construction was started in 1632. More than 20,000 workmen worked for 20 years to complete it. If machines were available in that age, work would have been much easier and faster.

How do Machines Help us?

Let us consider some of the machines that we use in our daily life. Match the machines in column A with the jobs given in column B in Table 12.1 (Fig. 12.1).

Table 12.1 Common machines and their uses

Column A	Column B
1. A pulley	lifting a big rock
2. A crowbar	lifting up the wheel of a car
3. Tongs	drawing water from the well
4. Screw jack	holding a hot piece of burning coal

All these machines help us in any one or more of the following ways:

 (i)   to multiply a force
 (ii) to do the job with less force or effort
 (iii) to apply the force in a more convenient direction
 (iv) to do a job which would otherwise be dangerous

Now identify in which way each of these machines in Figure 12.1 help us. (They may help us in one or more of the mentioned ways.)

(a) Pulley

(b) Crowbar

(c) Tongs

(d) Screw jack

Fig. 12.1   Some common machines

How do Machines Work?

Machines do not work on their own. They need the *effort* (or energy) of some external agent. Each of the machine mentioned here needs the *muscular energy* of the machine operator. Electrical machines need *electrical energy*. Windmills and turbines need *wind* and *water*.

Heavy machinery is made up of simple machines. A compound machine like a computer has numerous simple machines in it.

Let us study in detail about these simple machines and the functions they perform (Fig. 12.2).

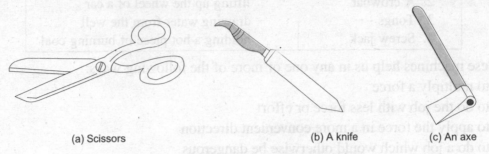

(a) Scissors   (b) A knife   (c) An axe

Fig. 12.2   Some common simple machines

Recall

- Machines are devices which help us to do our work faster and with less effort.
- Machines need energy from some external source in order to work.

Let's Answer

1. Name a machine that is operated using the following energy:
   (i) sun   (ii) coal   (iii) diesel
2. Which source of energy is used to operate a remote-controlled toy car?

TYPES OF SIMPLE MACHINES

Simple machines are of various types as listed here.

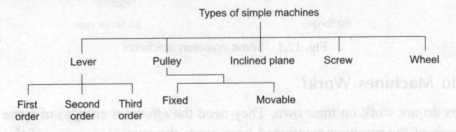

Levers

A *lever* consists of a rigid bar which is free to turn about a fixed point called its *fulcrum*. A simple example of a lever is a crowbar that helps us to lift loads that we cannot lift easily otherwise.

In Figure 12.3 the straight iron bar serves as a crowbar and helps to lift up the heavy rock.

The *weight* of the object that is to be moved or lifted is called the *load*. The force applied to lift the load is called the *effort*. The point on which the rod is supported and about which it can turn is called the *fulcrum* (Fig. 12.3).

Fig. 12.3   A man using a crowbar to lift a rock

A lever allows you to lift or move a large load with a small effort, i.e., it gives you an advantage. This advantage is called the mechanical advantage of the lever and is given as

$$Mechanical\ advantage = Load/Effort \qquad (1)$$

Law of Levers

The law of levers states that

$$load \times load\ arm = effort \times effort\ arm$$

The distance of the load from the fulcrum is called the *load arm*. The distance of the effort from the fulcrum is called the *effort arm* (Fig. 12.4).

Let us understand this with the help of a few activities.

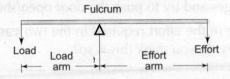

Fig. 12.4   A typical lever

 **Activity 1**

To demonstrate the law of levers.

Materials required   Weighing machine, see-saw, measuring tape.

Method   Weigh yourself and your friend on the same weighing machine and note down your weights. Now you and your friend sit on the two opposite ends of the see-saw. Find the positions on the see-saw at which you and your friend balance each other i.e. when the plank is horizontal. Mark the positions and measure the distance of yourself and that of your friend from the fulcrum (the centre of the see-saw) (Fig. 12.5).

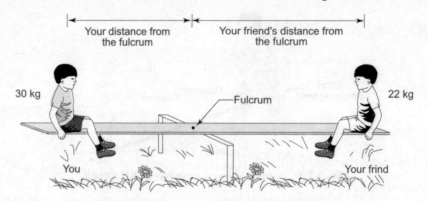

Fig. 12.5   The law of levers

Multiply as shown. Your weight × your distance from the fulcrum. Your friend's weight × his/her distance from the fulcrum.

What do you find if you compare the two products?

Your weight × distance from the fulcrum = your friend's weight × his/her distance from the fulcrum.

 Activity 2

A door (or gate) may be considered as a lever with the hinge as the fulcrum, the weight of the door as the load and the force you apply to push the door open or shut as the effort. Place your hand near the edge of the door and try to push the door open/shut. Now place your hand close to the hinges and try to push the door open/shut.

Do you find any difference in the effort required in the two cases? If yes, then in which case is the effort more? Why do you think this is so?

SOLVED EXAMPLES

Example 1   If you are able to lift a stone of 250 kg wt by applying a force of only 10 kg wt, what is the mechanical advantage of your lever?

Solution

$$\text{Mechanical advantage} = \frac{\text{Load}}{\text{Effort}} = \frac{250}{10} = 25$$

Examples 2   Shankar uses a force of 27 kg wt at a distance of 480 cm from the fulcrum of a crowbar to lift a rock placed 24 cm away from the fulcrum (Fig. 12.6). What is the weight of the rock? What is its mechanical advantage?

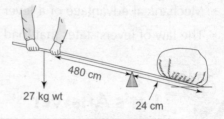

Solution

Fig. 12.6

Effort = 27 kg wt; Effort arm = 480 cm;

Load arm = 24 cm; Load = ?

We know from the law of levers that

Load × Load arm = Effort × Effort arm

$$\text{Load} = \frac{\text{Effort} \times \text{Effort arm}}{\text{Load arm}} = \frac{27 \times 480}{24} = 540$$

∴   Weight of the rock = 540 kg wt

Mechanical advantage = Load/Effort = 540/27 = 20.

Example 3   Sunita and Vanita sit on the opposite ends of a see-saw. If Sunita weighs 32 kg wt and sits at a distance of 180 cm from the fulcrum of the see-saw, where should Vanita weighing 36 kg wt sit in order that the see-saw be made horizontal?

Solution We know that

Load × Load arm = Effort × Effort arm

Load = 36 kg wt; Effort = 32 kg wt; Effort arm = 180 cm

$$\text{Load arm} = \frac{\text{Effort} \times \text{Effort arm}}{\text{Load}} = \frac{32 \times 180}{36} = 160 \text{ cm}$$

∴ Vanita has to sit at a distance of 160 cm from the fulcrum of the see-saw to make it horizontal.

Recall

- A lever consists of a rigid bar which is free to turn about a fixed point called its fulcrum.
- The weight of the object that is to be moved or lifted is called the *load*.
- The force applied to lift the load is called the *effort*.
- Mechanical advantage of a lever = load/effort.
- The law of levers states that load × load arm = effort × effort arm.

Let's Answer

1. Prakash lifts a stone of 500 kg wt using a crow bar, with the stone at 10 cm from the fulcrum. At what distance from the fulcrum should he apply a force of 50 kg wt to lift the stone?

   (1 m)

2. Rahul weighing 70 kg wt and Priyanka weighing 40 kg wt sit on opposite ends of a see-saw. If Rahul sits at a distance of 100 cm from the fulcrum, where should Priyanka sit, to exactly balance the see-saw? (175 cm from fulcrum)

Classes of Levers

Depending on the position of the fulcrum, load and effort, levers are classified into three classes or orders (Fig. 12.7).

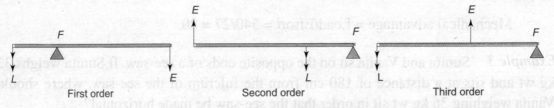

First order   Second order   Third order

Fig. 12.7   Various classes of levers

Levers of the first order   In such levers, the fulcrum is between the load and the effort, e.g., a pair of scissors, see-saw, beam balance, shears, crowbar, etc.

Levers of the second order   In these kind of levers, the fulcrum is at one end, the effort is applied at the other end and the load is in the middle, e.g., wheelbarrow, nutcracker, bottle-opener, etc.

Levers of the third order   In levers of the third order, the fulcrum is at one end, the load is applied at the other end and the effort is applied in the middle, e.g., the human forearm, forceps, broom, fishing rods, tongs, etc.

Remember: F, L and *E* in each of the three levers must be in the centre in turn. In the first order of levers, *F* is in the centre. In the second order of levers, *L* is in the centre. In the third order of levers, *E* is in the centre.

Can you guess which order of levers will always have a mechanical advantage greater than 1?

Remember: $MA = \dfrac{\text{Load}}{\text{Effort}}$; load × load arm = effort × effort arm

or $MA = \dfrac{\text{Effort arm}}{\text{Load arm}}$

Therefore, a second order lever will always have MA greater than 1.

Efficiency, Velocity Ratio and Mechanical Advantage

If no energy is lost by a machine then by the principle of conservation of energy, the total energy given out or work done by the machine in a given time should be equal to the total energy given to or work done on the machine, in the same interval of time. However, such a machine would be an ideal machine.

In any machine, work done by the machine in a given time will always be less than the work done on the machine in the same interval of time. This is because some energy is always lost due to friction.

For any machine,

$$\text{Efficiency} = \frac{\text{Work done by the machine in a given time}}{\text{Work done on the machine in the same time}} \times 100 \qquad (3)$$

Efficiency of a machine is always less than (or in ideal cases equal to) 100%.

We now introduce a new term known as *velocity ratio*.

$$\text{Velocity Ratio} = \frac{\text{Distance moved by the effort}}{\text{Distance moved by the load}} \qquad (4)$$

Thus, for any machine, efficiency can also be written as

$$\frac{\text{Load} \times \text{Distance moved by load}}{\text{Effort} \times \text{Distance moved by effort}} \times 100$$

$$\text{Mechanical advantage} = \left(\frac{\text{Efficiency}}{100}\right) \times \text{Velocity Ratio} \qquad (5)$$

Work done by a force = Force × distance moved in the direction of the force

The unit of work is joule (J).   1 J = 1 N × 1 m

A pair of levers acting together forms a most useful machine. The fulcrum is at the point where the two blades are riveted together, e.g., scissors, tongs, nutcracker, pliers, etc. The effort is applied at one end, while the load is at the point where the blades cut the material.

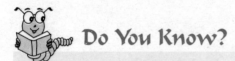

Do You Know?

The human body is a very complex machine. Normally, a machine is made to perform only certain specific jobs. But the human body can carry out a wide variety of jobs. The muscular system and skeletal system enable us to perform many different types of movements. There are several parts in the human body which can function as levers.

The diagrams in Figure 12.8 show how three organs of the human body function as levers. Can you guess what order of lever each of them is?

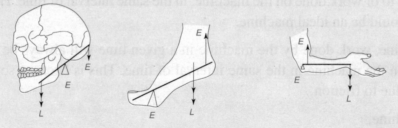

Fig. 12.8   Levers in the human body

Railway platform balance and steel yard

You must have seen heavy luggage being weighed on a railway platform balance. The *railway platform balance* is also a lever. In a ration shop or in factories, you must have seen heavy bags of rice, flour, etc., being weighed. This weighing machine is called a *steel yard*.

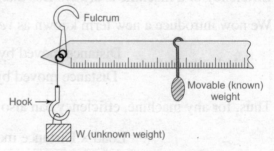

Fig. 12.9   A steel yard

A steel yard is a lever in which one arm is longer than the other. The substance to be weighed is hung from a hook as shown in Figure 12.9. On the other side of the fulcrum, a known weight is moved to a position where the lever is balanced. The longer arm of the lever is often marked in kilograms, so that the weight *W* can be found out directly. Such weighing machines are also seen in doctor's clinics and hospitals.

Recall

- Levers are classified into three classes/orders depending on the position of the load, the effort and the fulcrum.

- Efficiency of a machine = $\dfrac{\text{Work done by the machine in a given time}}{\text{Work done on the machine in the same time}} \times 100$

- Efficiency of a machine is always less than 100%.

- Mechanical advantage = $\dfrac{\text{Efficiency}}{100} \times \text{Velocity Ratio}$

Let's Answer

1. Which of the following levers will have the greatest mechanical advantage?
   (i) A lever whose load arm = effort arm
   (ii) A lever whose effort arm > load arm
   (iii) A lever whose load arm (slightly) > effort arm

2. Look at the various kinds of levers shown in Figure 12.10. Identify the class/order to which each lever belongs. Mark clearly the load, effort and fulcrum as *L*, *E* and *F*.

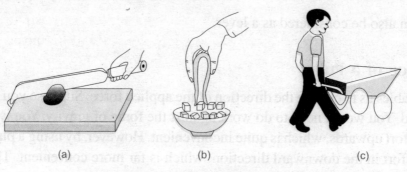

(a)   (b)   (c)

Fig. 12.10 Various kinds of levers

PULLEYS

In your Mechano set, you have yet another kind of simple machine. It is a *pulley*. A pulley consists of a *wheel* with a groove in it, over which a rope can be passed. The pulley moves around an *axle* fixed to a support which is called a *block*.

Pulleys are used in cranes, lifts, and to draw water from wells.

Fixed and movable pulleys

A pulley can be *fixed* or *movable*. In a fixed pulley, the block is fixed. In a movable pulley, the block is movable and the pulley along with its block moves with the load (Fig. 12.11).

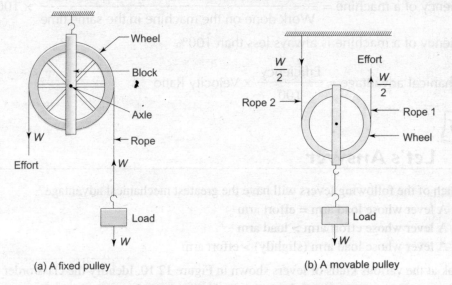

(a) A fixed pulley   (b) A movable pulley

Fig. 12.11 The two types of pulleys

A pulley can also be considered as a lever.

Importance of a Pulley

A pulley enables us to change the direction of the applied force. Suppose you had to lift up a heavy load. You would need to do work against the force of gravity. You would have to apply the effort upwards, which is quite inconvenient. However, by using a pulley, you can apply the effort in the downward direction, which is far more convenient. Thus, a pulley allows us to apply the effort in a convenient direction.

Mechanical Advantage of a Pulley

Let us now determine the mechanical advantage of a pulley.

Fixed pulley   Vijay uses a fixed pulley to draw out water from a well. The mass of the bucket is 5 kg. Vijay pulls the rope down by 2 m. What is the work done by Vijay?

The downward force on the bucket of water (due to gravity) = $5 \times 9.8 = 49$ N. If the rope is pulled down by 2 m, the bucket moves up by 2 m.

$\therefore$ Work done on the bucket = 49 N $\times$ 2 m = 98 J = work done by Vijay

Thus, in a fixed pulley, there is no gain in work because the load and the effort are equal.

The mechanical advantage of a fixed pulley is 1.

Movable pulley   In a movable pulley, the load to be lifted is distributed equally between the ropes 1 and 2, i.e., the rope which is fixed at one end takes up half the load, so the effort you need to apply on rope 2 to lift the load is only half the load (Fig. 12.11).

In this case, the mechanical advantage of a movable pulley is 2. However, rope 2 has to be pulled upwards, which is inconvenient. This can be avoided by using a combination of a fixed and a movable pulley (Fig. 12.12). The fixed pulley here only serves the function of changing the direction in which the effort has to be applied. Now you have to pull rope 3 downwards with an effort which is only half the load.

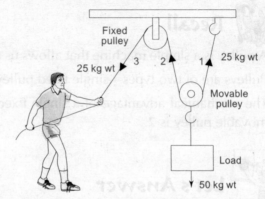

Fig. 12.12   Combination of fixed and movable pulley

If the two-pulley system shown here is used to lift a load of 400 kg wt, what is the effort needed to be applied? What is the mechanical advantage?

Wheel-and-Axle

It consists of a wheel of radius R attached to an axle of smaller radius r. Both rotate about a common axis. One end of the rope passing over the wheel is attached to an axle while effort is applied at the other end. Another rope passes over the axle in the opposite direction (Fig. 12.13).

When the wheel rotates, the rope on the wheel is unwound. Since the axle is firmly attached to the wheel, the wheel also rotates the axle such that the rope on the axle is wound up causing the load to be lifted up.

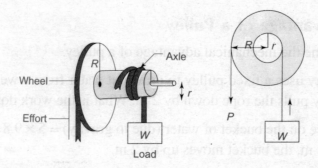

Fig. 12.13 Effort is applied in downward (convenient) direction, load is moved upwards

$$\text{Mechanical advantage} = \frac{\text{Load}}{\text{Effort}} = \frac{\text{Radius of the wheel }(R)}{\text{Radius of the axle }(r)}$$

The principle of wheel-and-axle is widely used these days in a number of devices, such as, in gear-boxes for automobiles.

Recall

- A pulley is a simple machine that allows us to apply the effort in a convenient direction.
- Pulleys are of two types—single fixed pulleys and single movable pulleys.
- The mechanical advantage of a single fixed pulley is always 1, while that for a single movable pulley is 2.

Let's Answer

1. What is the mechanical advantage of a single fixed pulley?
2. Why is it preferable to use a fixed and movable pulley combination rather than a single movable pulley?
3. What is the mechanical advantage of a wheel and axle?

INCLINED PLANE

The inclined plane is a simple machine which is used to raise heavy loads easily by rolling them along an inclined surface rather than lifting them up vertically. Stairs, escalators and ramps are examples of inclined planes.

Heavy barrels are loaded into trucks by pushing them along an inclined plane made of a wooden plank (Fig. 12.14).

In order to raise the barrel through the height *AB*, it has to be pushed (rolled) through a greater distance *BC* when an inclined plane is used. Still this requires lesser effort than raising the barrel vertically upwards. The *steeper* the slope, the *greater* is the effort needed to push the load up.

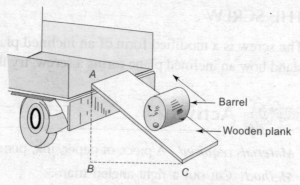

Fig. 12.14   An inclined plane

 Activity 3

Materials required   Wooden block, spring balance, cardboard, pile of books, table.

Method   Take a wooden block and measure its weight using a spring balance. Now make an inclined plane by resting one edge of the cardboard on a pile of books, while the other edge rests on the table (Fig. 12.15).

(a) Apply an effort on the wooden block using the spring balance, so that the block just moves up the inclined plane. You will find that the spring balance reads less than the weight of the block.

(b) Change the angle of inclination of the plane by adding some books.

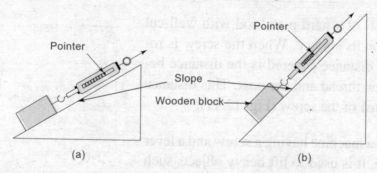

Fig. 12.15   Importance of slope in an inclined plane

What do you observe? The reading on the spring balance changes. In which case is the reading greater?

The reading on the spring balance is greater for (b) because the slope of the inclined plane is steeper.

Another example of an inclined plane is a wedge. For example, an axe is a wedge with two inclined surfaces.

THE SCREW

The screw is a modified form of an inclined plane which has circular motion. To understand how an inclined plane forms a screw, try the following activity.

Activity 4

Materials required A piece of paper, ink, pencil, scale.

Method Cut out a right-angled triangle from a piece of paper. Its slanting surface is the inclined surface. Colour the inclined surface with ink. Wrap the paper around the pencil keeping the base line horizontal. See how the sloping side of the paper goes round and round the pencil. Compare it with a screw and a spiral staircase. Draw a line down the paper while it is still rolled around the pencil. Now unroll the paper. Join the lines to make steps as shown in Figure 12.16.

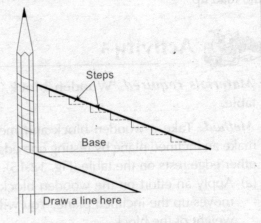

Fig. 12.16   An inclined plane forms the screw

A screw consists of a hard metal rod with well-cut spiral threads on its surface. When the screw is rotated once, the distance covered is the distance between one screw thread and the next. This distance is called the *pitch* of the screw (Fig. 12.17).

A screw jack is a machine having a screw and a lever in combination. It is used to lift heavy objects such as cars, buses, trucks, etc.

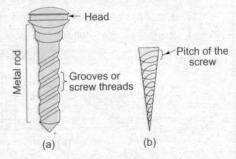

Fig. 12.17   A screw

You must have noticed that a carpenter prefers a screw to an ordinary nail. This is because the threads of the screw grip the wood firmly such that the screw cannot be pulled out easily. It has to be unscrewed in the opposite direction to be pulled out.

THE WHEEL

The wheel is also a simple machine. Wheels help to move objects with very little force. They also help to reduce friction because the force of friction to be overcome while rolling a body over a surface is much less than the force of friction to be overcome in sliding the body over the same surface, i.e.,

Rolling friction < Sliding friction

 **Recall**

- An inclined plane is a device that helps to reduce the effort required for raising a heavy load. The lesser the slope of the inclined plane, the lesser is the effort needed.
- A screw is a modified form of an inclined plane.
- Wheels help to move heavy objects by reducing the force of friction to be overcome.
- All complicated machines are a combination of various simple machines.

EXERCISES

1. **Give one word answers for the following**
   (a) The fixed point about which the lever can turn.
   (b) A simple machine that helps to reduce friction.
   (c) A machine that consists of a pair of inclined planes.
   (d) A lever of second order.
   (e) The ratio of load to effort of a machine.
   (f) A simple machine that helps us to apply the effort in a convenient direction.
   (g) A modified form of an inclined plane.
   (h) A machine that helps to move a big rock.

2. **Mark the following sentences as *True* or *False***
   (a) In a beam balance, the load arm and effort arm are equal.
   (b) A wheelbarrow is a lever of the first order.
   (c) A movable pulley helps us to apply the effort in a convenient direction.
   (d) A crowbar helps us to move a load faster.
   (e) The mechanical advantage of a single fixed pulley is more than that of a single movable pulley.
   (f) A pair of scissors and a pair of tongs are levers of the same order.
   (g) Levers, pulleys, inclined planes, screws, and wheels are simple machines.
   (h) A wheel is a modified form of an inclined plane.

3. **Answer the following questions briefly**
   (a) What are the different ways in which machines help us? Give one example of a machine that helps us in each of these ways.
   (b) State the law of levers.

(c) Define the terms (a) effort (b) load (c) fulcrum (d) load arm (e) effort arm, with respect to a lever.

(d) Explain mechanical advantage, velocity ratio and efficiency of a machine, giving their mathematical expressions. What is an ideal machine and what is its efficiency? Why is this not achievable in practice?

(e) What is a pulley? What are the two different types of pulleys?

(f) Explain with the help of a diagram, how the mechanical advantage of a movable pulley is greater than 1?

(g) What is an inclined plane? When is it used?

(h) What are the uses of the screw and the wheel?

(i) In each of the levers shown in Figure 12.18, identify the positions of the effort, load and the fulcrum. State the order of lever in each example.

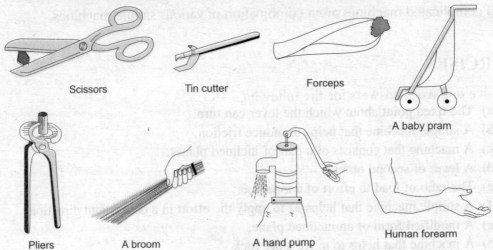

Fig. 12.18   Different types of levers

(j) Explain the classification of levers. On what basis are they classified?

Numerical Problems

1. The effort arm of a lever is 7.5 m long and the load arm is 3 m long. What is the effort needed to raise a load of 60 kg wt? What is the mechanical advantage of this lever?

2. Two children, each of weight 40 kg wt, sit together on the same side of a see-saw at a distance of 1.5 m from the fulcrum. Where must a boy weighing 60 kg wt sit in order to balance these children?

3. A man applied an effort of 50 kg wt to a crowbar to lift a rock of 750 kg wt. The distance of the rock from the fulcrum is 10 cm. How far from the fulcrum should the man apply the effort?

4. A man wishes to lift a sack of rice of weight 650 kg wt. If he uses

   (a) a single fixed pulley, how much effort will he need to apply? What will be the mechanical advantage?

(b) a single movable pulley, how much effort will he have to apply? What will be the mechanical advantage? Will he be able to apply the effort in a convenient direction? What means would you suggest to make the process more convenient?

Answers

1. 40 kg wt; 1.5
2. 2 m from fulcrum on the other side
3. 1.5 m
4. (a) 60 kg wt; 1 (b)30 kg wt; 2. No. He should use a combination of a single fixed pulley and a single movable pulley.

THINK AND ANSWER

1. A knife, a chisel and an axe are examples of two inclined planes put together. Can you think how the inclined planes help in the function of these tools?
2. Why are mountain roads built in the form of spirals going round and round the mountain rather than directly up the slope?
3. Where do you see spiral staircases being used? What would be the advantage of a spiral staircase over an ordinary staircase or ramp?
4. Explain why
   (a) the handles of tin shears are kept much longer than the blade.
   (b) there is not much difference between the length of the handle and the blades in an ordinary scissors used for cutting paper or cloth.
   (c) levers of class II necessarily multiply the force.
   (d) we prefer inclined planes that slope up gradually for lifting heavy loads.
5. Radha and Raja were using a stapler to staple their papers together. Radha pressed down at the front end of the stapler, while Raja pressed down near the middle of the stapler. Radha finished the job faster and her fingers were less tired as compared to Raja. Why?
6. In Meera's refrigerator, the ice tray had got stuck in the freezer due to ice having formed all around it. Meera's mother took a long, flat metal spoon, inserted a part of it under one end of the ice tray and pressed downwards at the other end of the spoon. The ice tray was dislodged very easily. Why?

 Teacher's Notes

- Students could be made to identify classes of levers out of a mixed collection of tweezers, staplers, scissors, nail cutter, can opener, etc.
- The class could be asked to identify various simple machines in a complex piece of machinery.
- Students could be assigned to write on various simple machines that they use in their daily lives.

13

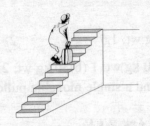

- Energy
- Mechanical energy—kinetic energy and potential energy
- Principle of conservation of energy
- Sources of energy
- Conserving our energy sources

Work and Energy

We perform a lot of activities everyday. Energy obtained from food is used by us to do these activities. Somedays, we feel very energetic and do a lot of work. There are also days when we do not have much energy and cannot do much work. To do a difficult or strenuous piece of work, we need to use more energy.

WORK

Work is a form of energy. When is work said to be done? Consider these examples:
- (a) Rajiv pushes a book across the table [Fig. 13.1(a)].
- (b) Amit pushes hard against the wall but is unable to make it move [Fig. 13.1(b)].
- (c) Rahul carries a heavy suitcase up the stairs [Fig. 13.1 (c)].

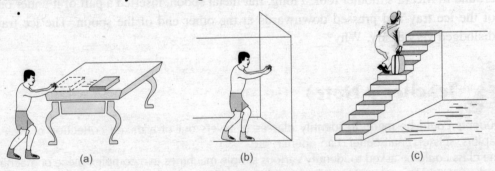

Fig. 13.1   Different forms of work

Whenever we apply a force on an object, and the point where the force is applied changes its position in the direction of the force, we say work is done. Thus, in the above examples, work is done in (a) and (c), but no work is done in (b).

We may apply force to raise or lower an object or to move it from one place to another. We may also apply force to change the shape of the object, e.g., kneading the dough or creating beautiful shapes out of plasticine or modelling clay. All this involves work.

Work is done when
- a force is applied on an object;
- the point where the force is applied changes its position (either by displacing the whole object or changing its shape).

Activity 1

(a) Lift a science book from the floor to your study table.

(b) Try to move a heavy boulder.

Do you do work in both the cases?

Measurement of Work

We have now understood what work is and when it is said to be done. But how do we measure the work done?

Let us take a few examples:

(a) Robin pushes a box of mass 5 kg through a distance of 1 m. Ravi pushes a box of mass 10 kg through the same distance of 1 m [Fig. 13.2 (a)].

(b) Lalita picks up two watermelons, each of mass 3 kg from the ground. She places the first one on a table of height 1 m and the other on a shelf of height 3 m [Fig. 13.2 (b)].

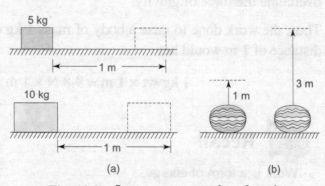

Fig. 13.2 Some more examples of work

In example (a), we say that Ravi does more work than Robin. In example (b), we say that Lalita does more work to lift the second melon than the first. Work done is more, either when the force applied is more or when the distance by which the object moves is greater.

Work is given by the product of the force applied on the object and the distance moved by the object in the direction of the force.

Work done (W) = Force (F) × Distance moved in the direction of the force (s).

Unit of Work

The unit of work is joule, abbreviated as J.

If a force of 1 N acting on a body makes it move through a distance of 1 m in the direction of the force, then the work done is said to be 1 J.

$$1 \text{ J} = 1 \text{ N} \times 1 \text{ m}$$

SOLVED EXAMPLES

Example   A force of 100 N moves a body through a distance of 4.5 m in the direction of the force. Calculate the work done.

Solution

Work done = Force × Distance moved = 100 N × 4.5 m = 450 J

∴ Work done = 450 J

We have learnt earlier that the weight of a body is the force of gravity acting on it. We also know that 1 kg wt = 9.8 N. When a body is moved vertically upwards, work is done to overcome the force of gravity.

Thus, the work done to raise a body of mass 1 kg or weight 1 kg wt vertically through a distance of 1 m would be:

$$1 \text{ kg wt} \times 1 \text{ m} = 9.8 \text{ N} \times 1 \text{ m} = 9.8 \text{ J}$$

 Recall

- Work is a form of energy.
- Work is done when a force is applied on an object and the point where the force is applied changes its position or its shape.
- Work done = force × distance moved in the direction of the force.

- The unit of work is joule. 1 J = 1 Nm
- Work done to raise an object of mass 1 kg or weight 1 kg wt vertically through a distance of 1 m is 9.8 J.

Let's Answer

1. What is the work done when Mohan lifts a sack of flour of mass 25 kg from a height of 15 m to a height of 30 m?
2. Suppose a box of mass 10 kg is moved horizontally along the floor through a distance of 1 m. What is the work done against the force of gravity? (Fig. 13.3) (*Remember:* Work done = force × distance moved in the direction of the force).

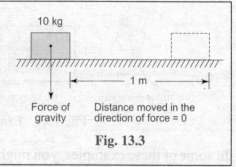

Fig. 13.3

ENERGY

The amount of work we do everyday depends on the amount of energy we have.

Energy is the capacity to do work.

A body which is capable of doing work is said to have energy, while a body which is not capable of doing work does not have any energy.

Various Forms of Energy

We need different kinds of energy for doing different kinds of work. For example,

- To boil water, we need *heat* energy.
- To lift or move an object, we need *mechanical* energy.
- In all our body movements, we use *muscular* energy.
- A noise or music you hear possesses *sound* energy.
- An electrical appliance needs *electrical* energy to operate.
- Chemical reactions taking place in a cell give *chemical* energy.
- A glowing light bulb gives us *light* energy.
- A piece of paper flies away due to *wind* energy.

Identify the various forms of energy in each of the following:

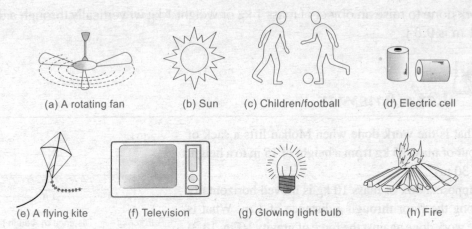

(a) A rotating fan   (b) Sun   (c) Children/football   (d) Electric cell

(e) A flying kite   (f) Television   (g) Glowing light bulb   (h) Fire

Fig. 13.4   Examples of various forms of energy

In some of these examples, you might have identified several forms of energy in the same object. What does this tell us? Energy of one form may be used to produce energy of other forms. In fact, energy of one form is constantly being changed into other forms. This is known as the *transformation of energy*.

Thus, when a girl plays a sitar, the *muscular energy* of her fingers is transformed into the *mechanical energy* of the vibrating string, which is then transformed into *sound energy* in the form of the beautiful music that you hear. When a fuel like wood is burnt, *chemical energy* is released and transformed into *heat and light energies*. A cell has chemical reactions going on inside it and the *chemical energy* from these reactions is transformed into the *electrical energy* which has many other uses.

Now go back to the examples in Figure 13.4, and try to identify the kind of energy transformation that takes place in each. Write down the energy transformations as in the example below:

A rotating fan   electrical energy → mechanical energy → wind energy

 Recall

- Energy is defined as the capacity to do work.
- There are different forms of energy such as heat, light, sound, mechanical, chemical, electrical, muscular, and wind energy.
- Energy can always be transformed from one form into another and this is known as transformation of energy.

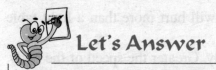
1. What types of energy transformations occur when you
   (i) rub the palms of your hands together to warm them in winter?
   (ii) burst a firecracker during Diwali?

MECHANICAL ENERGY

Mechanical energy is the energy associated with the mechanical work done by objects.

It is of two types — kinetic energy and potential energy.

Kinetic Energy

Consider these examples:
  (a) A moving cricket ball hits the stumps and knocks off the stumps [Fig. 13.5 (a)].

(a)   (b)

Fig. 13.5   Kinetic energy

  (b) A stone thrown at a glass window breaks the glass [Fig. 13.5 (b)].
  (c) The rotating blades of a grinder crush the spices to a fine powder.

All these examples show that moving objects possess energy.
The energy that an object possesses by virtue of its motion is called kinetic energy.

Factors influencing kinetic energy

There are two factors which influence kinetic energy, namely,
  1. Kinetic energy depends upon the *mass* of the body. Greater the mass of the body, greater is its kinetic energy.

213

For example, a heavy cricket ball thrown at you will hurt more than a light table tennis ball thrown with the same speed.

2. Kinetic energy depends upon the *speed* of the body. Greater the speed of the body, greater is its kinetic energy. For example, a fast-moving truck crashing into a wall can cause more damage than a slow-moving truck striking the same wall.

Potential Energy

Let us understand what potential energy is by taking some examples:

(a) During an avalanche or landslide, huge rocks and boulders come rushing down the mountain side and destroy objects lying below. Before the landslide, these rocks were at rest on top of the mountain.

How did they possess so much energy to cause such destruction? Will the destructive effect be more if the rocks fall from a lesser height or from a greater height? Will the destruction be more, if the rocks were massive or small?

(b) Raju places an arrow in the bow and stretches the bow string. When he releases the bow string, the arrow shoots forward and hits Sudhir who gets hurt.

Will the arrow hurt Sudhir more, if Raju had stretched the bow string only a little or if he had stretched it much more?

In (a), when the stone was at rest on top of the mountain, it had energy stored in it. This energy was used to do work when the stone fell down. The stone possesses energy because of its height above the ground.

In (b), the stretched bow string, though at rest, has energy stored in it. When the bow is released, this energy is used to do work to push forward the arrow. The stretched bow string possesses energy because it is deformed.

In the examples discussed, the stone and the bow are both stationary but still they possess energy.

The energy that a stationary object possesses by virtue of its position (i.e., height with respect to the surface of the earth) or configuration (whether it is stretched or compressed, pushed or pulled to one side) is called its potential energy.

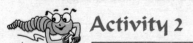 Activity 2

Place a piece of glass on the floor. Take a stone, raise it to a certain height and drop it on the piece of glass. What happens? Can you explain why?

Factors influencing potential energy

The following two factors influence potential energy:

1. Potential energy depends upon the *height* of the object above the surface of the earth. Greater the height, greater is the potential energy.
2. Potential energy depends upon the *change in configuration* (stretching/compression, etc.) of an object. Greater the change in configuration, greater is the potential energy.
3. Greater the *mass* of the object, greater is the potential energy.

When a body possesses potential energy, it has to be changed into some other form of energy before it can be used. For instance, a stationary rock on top of a mountain is not dangerous until its potential energy changes into kinetic energy, i.e., until it begins to roll down the mountain (Fig. 13.6).

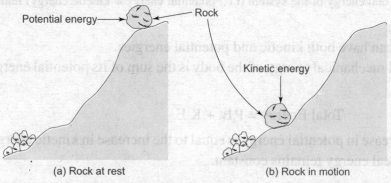

Potential energy → Rock

Kinetic energy

(a) Rock at rest

(b) Rock in motion

Fig. 13.6   Conversion of potential energy into kinetic energy

Can you think of a situation where an object has both potential energy and kinetic energy? Consider the following example:

(a) When a ball is thrown vertically upwards and is rising up, it is moving up with some speed. Thus it has *kinetic* energy. It is also at a certain height above the ground, so it has *potential* energy. As the ball rises in height, its speed reduces, its *kinetic* energy is changed to *potential* energy. At its maximum height, the ball stops momentarily and here it possesses only *potential* energy.

As the ball comes down, its speed increases as the height decreases. Thus its *potential* energy decreases while its *kinetic* energy increases. When the ball just reaches the ground, it has only *kinetic* energy (Fig. 13.7).

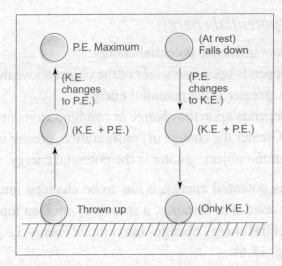

P.E. Maximum
(At rest)
Falls down
(K.E. changes to P.E.)
(P.E. changes to K.E.)
(K.E. + P.E.)
(K.E. + P.E.)
Thrown up
(Only K.E.)

Fig. 13.7 Total energy of the system (i.e., potential energy + kinetic energy) remains constant

Thus,

- A body can have both kinetic and potential energies.
- The total mechanical energy of the body is the sum of its potential energy and kinetic energy:

$$\text{Total Energy} = \text{P.E.} + \text{K.E.}$$

- The decrease in potential energy is equal to the increase in kinetic energy, so the total mechanical energy remains constant.

Activity 3

To make a magic tin

Materials required   A small tin with a lid, a rubber band, a small heavy stone, hammer, nail.

Method   Make a pair of holes directly above one another on each end of the tin as shown in Figure 13.8. Stretch a rubber band across the holes and tie the stone in the middle. Close the lid of the tin firmly. Now roll the tin on the ground. Notice the magic! The tin rolls forward for some distance, stops due to friction of the floor, but then it starts rolling back towards you and keeps rolling back and forth for a while. Can you explain why?

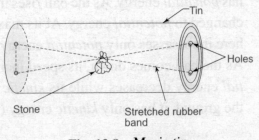

Fig. 13.8   Magic tin

PRINCIPLE OF CONSERVATION OF ENERGY

We have seen how energy can be converted from one form to another. Can you say how much energy of one kind will be obtained by transformation of a certain quantity of energy of another kind? This is given by the *principle of conservation of energy*.

Principle of conservation of energy

The principle of conservation of energy states that the total amount of energy in any system always remains constant, provided no additional energy is externally supplied or taken away from it. The energy can only be transformed from one form to another.

Recall

- Mechanical energy is the energy associated with the mechanical work done by objects. It can be either kinetic or potential energy.

- Kinetic energy is the energy that an object possesses by virtue of its motion. It depends upon the mass and the speed of the body.

- Potential energy is the energy possessed by a stationary object on account of its position or configuration. It depends upon the height above the earth's surface or a change in the configuration of the object and its mass.

- The total mechanical energy of a body is the sum of its potential energy and kinetic energy.

- The principle of conservation of energy states that the total amount of energy in any system always remains constant, provided no additional energy is externally supplied or taken away from it. Energy can only be transformed from one form to another.

Let's Answer

1. Write in two columns which of the following have potential energy/kinetic energy. (If you feel the object has neither, do not write it in either column. If you feel that the object has both, then write it in both the columns.)
   - (a) water stored in an overhead tank
   - (b) a running bus
   - (c) a stationary bus on the top of a mountain
   - (d) a compressed spring
   - (e) a stone lying on the ground
   - (f) a ball rolling along the ground
   - (g) a stretched rubber band
   - (h) a bird perched on a tree
   - (i) a bird flying in the sky
   - (j) a rapidly rotating wheel

SOURCES OF ENERGY

Nature has provided us with varied sources of energy, as described below.

Sun   The sun is one of the primary sources of energy in nature. It provides light and heat. Plants use the light from the sun to make their food. These plants, in turn, provide food to animals and human beings (Fig. 13.9).

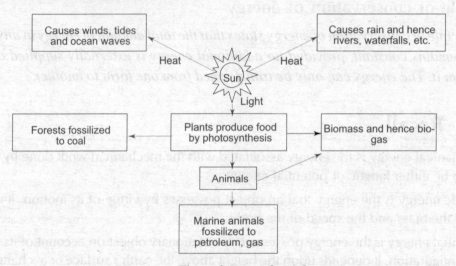

Fig. 13.9   Flow of energy from the sun

Wind   Wind is another source of mechanical energy. It is used to run windmills which in turn generate electricity to operate pumps, etc.

Water   The energy generated by waterfalls is used to generate electrical energy.

Radioactive elements   Uranium, thorium, plutonium, etc. (radioactive elements), are the raw materials to generate nuclear energy in nuclear reactors. Nuclear reactors can be used to run turbines to generate electricity. Nuclear energy has a lot of other applications in industry and scientific research.

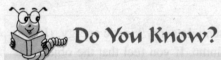 **Do You Know?**

Nuclear energy obtained from nuclear reactors could provide a much more efficient source of energy as compared to conventional fuels. Nuclear fuel, mainly uranium, is available in India at the Jaduguda mines in Bihar. Although the fuel is expensive and raises the problem of disposal of nuclear wastes, which often give out hazardous radiations, the amount of energy that can be generated by a nuclear reactor can be estimated from the fact that just 1 gram of uranium releases nearly 70 billion joules of energy! Compare this with the fact that 1 gram of coal gives out just about 30,000 joules of energy!

Earth The heat energy in the interior of the earth is called *geothermal* energy. In some places, this is manifested in the form of hot springs or geysers. This is also being tapped and put to a variety of uses.

Tides Tidal energy is another source of energy that is being used nowadays.

Biogas Energy from *biomass* in the form of biogas is used as an alternative for fuels.

Renewable and Non-Renewable Sources of Energy

Depending upon their availability the various sources of energy can be classified as renewable or non-renewable sources.

Renewable sources The energy sources which are constantly replenished by nature are called *renewable* sources of energy. For example, energy from the sun (solar energy), wind, water, etc.

Non-renewable sources Some sources of energy such as coal and petroleum take millions of years to be formed and they get exhausted with use. Such sources are called *non-renewable* sources of energy.

CONSERVING OUR ENERGY SOURCES

Can you think of ways in which you can save on energy at home?

You can save energy by turning off lights and fans when they are not really needed, by the judicious use of cooking gas, by pooling cars to save on petrol, etc.

The earth's reserves of non-renewable sources of energy are getting depleted. How can we conserve and find out newer energy resources for the future?

Some of the ways in which we can conserve our energy resources are by:

1. Judicious use of existing resources and reducing our dependence on the non-renewable sources of energy. The use of water and wind energies to generate electricity must be increased. Motor vehicles can be made to run on electricity or sunlight rather than petrol or diesel.
2. Use of biogas made from plant and animal waste as an alternative energy source.
3. Use of devices such as solar cells, solar cookers (Fig. 13.10), solar heaters, solar dryers, etc., which make use of solar energy.

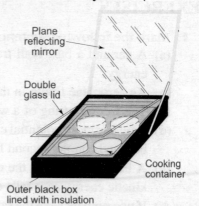

Fig. 13.10 A solar cooker

Recall

- There are different sources of energy such as sun, wind, waterfalls, fossil fuels, biogas, radioactive elements, etc. Tidal energy and geothermal energy are some other forms of energy.
- Renewable sources of energy are those which are being constantly replenished by nature, e.g., sun, wind.
- Non-renewable sources of energy are those that take millions of years to form and whose supply gets exhausted with use, e.g., coal, petroleum.
- Energy resources can be conserved in many ways.

Let's Answer

1. How do machines and instruments on man-made satellites obtain electricity for their functioning?

2. Find out how solar cells are used to generate electricity for street lighting (Fig. 13.11)?

3. Where can you use the energy obtained from a wind mill?

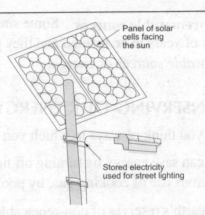

Panel of solar cells facing the sun

Stored electricity used for street lighting

Fig. 13.11 Solar cells used in street lighting

EXERCISES

1. **Mark the following sentences as *True* or *False***
   (a) A car and a bus, both travelling at the same speed have the same amount of kinetic energy.
   (b) An aeroplane flying in the sky has both potential and kinetic energies.
   (c) The wound spring of a watch has potential energy.
   (d) Raju has more potential energy when he stands on the first floor of the house than when he stands on the second floor.
   (e) A ball thrown from the roof top, at first has only potential energy, but later acquires kinetic energy as it falls down.
   (f) If two runners have the same mass, the one running faster will have more kinetic energy.

2. **Give one word answers for the following**
   (a) In which of the following cases is work being done?
       (i) A boy kicking a stone along the ground.
       (ii) Mohan pushes a boulder with a lot of force but the boulder does not move.
       (iii) Food is pushed from the mouth into the stomach.
       (iv) A stone is raised by 2 m and then lowered by 1 m.
       (v) Raju puts on the television and later switches it off.

   (b) Which of the following have potential energy/kinetic energy/neither/both?
       (i) A stationary ball on the ground.
       (ii) A ball thrown up in the air..
       (iii) A vibrating spring.
       (iv) A rocket shooting off into outer space.
       (v) A train running on level ground.
       (vi) A stationary man on the top of a hill.

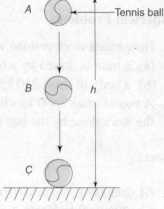

   (c) Figure 13.12 shows a tennis ball being dropped to the ground. *A* is its highest position, *B* is its position before it strikes the ground, *C* is its position when it strikes the ground. Indicate what kind of energy the ball has in positions *A*, *B* and *C*.

Fig. 13.12

   (d) What energy transformation takes place in each of the following:
       (i) a solar cell   (ii) a loudspeaker   (iii) an electric iron (iv) a steam engine
       (v) a rocket   (vi) a telephone receiver

   (v) Classify the following sources of energy as renewable/non-renewable:
       (i) kerosene   (ii) diesel   (iii) wind   (iv) tides
       (v) sun   (vi) firewood   (vii) coal   (viii) water

3. **Answer the following questions briefly**
   (a) When is work said to be done? What are the units in which work is measured? What is the relation between 1 J and 1 kg wt?
   (b) What is energy? List any five different forms of energy.
   (c) Define the terms potential energy and kinetic energy. Give examples. On what properties of the body does each depend?
   (d) State the principle of conservation of energy and give an example.
   (e) Explain renewable and non-renewable energy sources with an example.
   (f) Give two examples to show that the energy we use originally came from the sun.
   (g) Given here are a few figures. Identify in each, which position represents potential energy and which kinetic energy (Fig. 13.13).

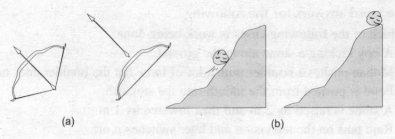

(a)

(b)

Fig. 13.13

Numerical Problems

1. How much work is done when
   (a) a train is driven by a force of 500 N through a distance of 400 m?
   (b) a body of mass 350 kg is raised to a height of 200 m?
2. A bus of mass 5000 kg climbs up a mountain through a vertical height of 400 m. What is the work done by the bus (in J and in kg wt m)?

Answers

1. (i) 200000 J   (ii) 686000 J   2. (i) 19600000 J
   (ii) 2000000 kg wt m

THINK AND ANSWER

1. How does the transformation of potential energy to kinetic energy and vice versa takes place in a spring, which is stretched or compressed and then released and allowed to vibrate?
2. Look at Figure 13.14. Which of the two children (assuming they have equal mass) has greater potential energy? Explain your answer. Which child will have greater kinetic energy on jumping down/ sliding down directly to the ground?

Fig. 13.14

Teacher's Notes

- Students can be taken on a visit to a nuclear reactor to see how nuclear energy is produced.
- The class can be asked to identify the energy transformations going on around them at home or in school.
- Models of a solar water heater, a solar cooker, a solar cell panel, and a biogas plant can be shown to the students as examples which use renewable sources of energy.

14

- Health
- Food for health
- Balanced diet
- Personal hygiene
  (a) oral hygiene, (b) eye care,
  (c) Hair care
- Community hygiene—living
  space, housing, sanitation,
  pollution, safe water
- Prevention of communicable
  diseases

Health and Hygiene

A healthy person can lead a happy life. But what does the word *health* mean to us?

Health is a state of the body when all the organs and organ systems function properly and the individual is free from any disease or discomfort. To remain healthy certain things have to be followed, such as,

(a) Proper food habits.
(b) Proper intake of water.
(c) Regular exercise.
(d) Personal hygiene and care of body organs.
(e) Public hygiene.

FOOD FOR HEALTH

Food is essential for growth and maintenance of our body. But taking in excess food or less amount of food could be harmful for our body.

Proper intake of food protects us from diseases, regulates our body functions and gives us the energy to perform various activities.

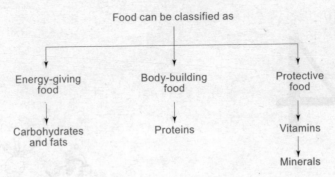

Fig. 14.1 Classification of food

The major nutrients and some common food materials in which they are found are given below:

Carbohydrates Wheat, rice, potato, sugar, jaggery, etc.

Proteins Milk, egg, meat, pulses, soya bean, etc.

Fats Butter, oil, ghee, etc.

Vitamins Green leafy vegetables and fruits.

Minerals Vegetables, meat, fish, egg, milk, pulses.

Water At least 8–10 glasses are required by the body everyday.

Roughage It is the fibrous substance found in raw vegetables and fruits. It contains no nutrients but helps in the regular movement of food through the alimentary canal.

Most of the food items that we consume have more than one type of nutrients.

Nowadays, the fashion of junk food or fried food such as chips, noodles, pizzas, burgers, wafers is causing *obesity,* i.e., increase in bulk and weight. Chocolates, candies and ice creams should be taken only once in a while because they contain a lot of calories. If one does not burn off these calories through exercise, participation in outdoor sports or other strenuous activities, then one becomes fat or *obese.*

A calorie is a measure of energy expenditure. It is a unit representing the energy provided by food. All food types, i.e., carbohydrates, proteins, and fats provide calories. Carbohydrate and protein have 4 calories per gram, and fat has 9 calories per gram.

BALANCED DIET

Usually our diet consists of chapatis/rice, pulses (dal), etc., so you can find a combination of all varieties of food.

 **Activity 1**

Make a chart of the food that you take in the morning, at noon and at night and collect the same information from some of your friends and then compare as shown in the Table 14.1.

Table 14.1

S.No.	Name of the student	Food item	Category of food
1.	Anil	Rice	Energy-giving food
2.			
3.			

A balanced diet is a diet which consists of

- an adequate proportion of carbohydrates, proteins, fats, vitamins, and minerals;
- an exact amount of raw materials needed for growth, development, repair, and replacement of worn out body tissues; and
- provides the right amount of energy required by the body.

The nutrients available in some food items which are part of our regular Indian diet are:

(a) Cereals → rich in carbohydrate.
(b) Vegetables such as lettuce (palak), cabbage, tomato, cauliflower → vitamins and fibres.
(c) Carrot → rich in vitamin A.
(d) Lemon juice → rich in vitamin C.
(e) Milk and milk products → rich in calcium.
(f) Brinjal, lettuce, apple → rich in iron.
(g) Seafood → rich in iodine.

Although a balanced diet is important, equally important is the right way of eating food. The following points should be kept in mind:

(a) good posture → sitting cross-legged or on a chair.
(b) correct proportion of food.
(c) chewing food properly, taking it in a relaxed manner.

A correct proportion of food is important because

- an inadequate quantity of proteins slows down the rate of growth and excess proteins can damage the kidneys.

- lack of carbohydrates can cause lethargy, while excess carbohydrates result in obesity.
- less intake of fat causes rough skin, weak eyesight and leanness, whereas excess fat can cause obesity and in extreme cases make the liver and pancreas inactive.

Water should also be considered as an important part of our diet. Intake of 8–10 glasses of water is a must. Those who drink a lesser quantity may suffer from jaundice, fatigue, kidney stones, and poor mental alertness. Depending upon physical exertion, or the temperature of the body, the consumption of water should be more when required.

Some Healthy Food Habits

Developing healthy food habits is simpler and easier than you might think. You will look and feel better if you make a habit of eating healthy food. You will have more energy and will concentrate better. Good food habits will make you stronger and you will rarely fall ill. The following points should be kept in mind for your diet to be healthy:

1. Eat food only when you are hungry.
2. Overeating should be avoided, even though you may find a dish very tasty.
3. Salads, raw vegetables and fruits should form an important part of the diet.
4. Fried and roasted food or spicy food should be avoided.
5. Food should not be taken in a hurry.
6. At least 8–10 glasses of water should be taken daily.
7. Food should be properly chewed before swallowing.
8. Too hot or too cold meals should be avoided.
9. Food which has been left over by others in the plate should not be consumed.

 Recall

- To remain healthy proper food habits, regular exercise, and proper intake of water are very essential.
- Physical health and mental health are interrelated.
- Food can be classified as energy-giving food (carbohydrates and fats), body-building food (proteins), and required protective foods (vitamins and minerals).
- A balanced diet should contain all the nutrients needed for proper growth and maintenance of the body.

Let's Answer

1. Why do you require food? What is a balanced diet?
2. Name the different food groups.
3. What are protective foods?
4. Name a few body-building foods.
5. Which food items provide energy?
6. Mention the harmful effects of junk food.

PERSONAL HYGIENE

It includes cleanliness of body parts both external and internal. The habit of keeping the body parts clean should be developed from childhood on. Otherwise, germs from various sources like dirt, can easily infect your body causing you to develop a disease. Some of the following habits can help you to maintain hygiene:

1. A regular bath is a must, as dirt deposited on the skin can cause itching and boils.
2. Hands should be washed clean before and after meals.
3. Nails should be trimmed and kept clean.
4. Eyes should be washed with cold water every few hours.
5. Never read in dim light or in light that is too bright—both can damage the eyes.
6. Rubbing the eyes, especially with unclean hands, should be avoided.
7. Matchsticks, pins, or knitting needles should never be used for removing wax from the ears.
8. Dirt should not be allowed to accumulate inside, outside or at the back of the ear as it may cause an infection.
9. Teeth should be cleaned after waking up and before going to sleep at night, preferably, even after each meal.
10. Hair should be regularly washed. A clean comb should be used to brush the hair.
11. Other people's towels should never be used.
12. It is advisable not to wear very tight clothes.
13. Only clean and washed clothes should be worn. Undergarments should be changed daily.
14. Food that we eat should be clean.
15. One should sleep in an airy room and never cover the face while sleeping.
16. Feet should be cleaned everyday and shoes should be well-fitting and comfortable.
17. Clean and regular toilet habits are important for maintaining good health.

227

Oral Hygiene

As we already know, an adult human has four different types of teeth (Fig. 14.2). They are fixed to the gums and are meant for chewing food.

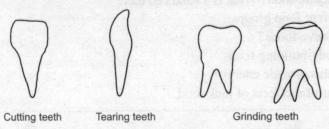

| Cutting teeth | Tearing teeth | Grinding teeth |

Fig. 14.2 The four different kinds of human teeth

The cutting teeth are also called *incisors*, the tearing teeth are termed *canines* and the grinding teeth are of two types, *pre-molars* and *molars*.

Each tooth has three different parts (Fig. 14.3).

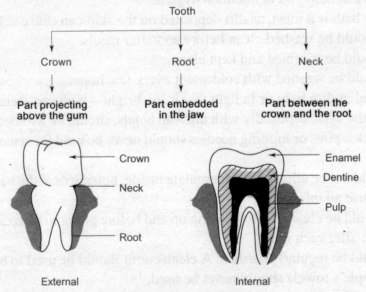

Fig. 14.3 Structure of the tooth

We all know that children love to eat chocolates, sweets, ice creams, toffees, etc. Once in a while it is not harmful but they should not become a regular part of the diet. This is because the sticky dissolved food in the mouth (saliva + chewed food) and harmful bacteria, together form the *plaque*, which damage teeth.

The thin layer of plaque on the teeth absorbs sugars like sponge. Bacteria in the plaque then changes this sugar into an acid which can dissolve the enamel, ultimately making a hole or cavity in the tooth. In addition, bacteria in plaque can also damage the gum tissue surrounding the tooth. The gums protect the teeth and the underlying bone. If gums become infected the bone that holds your teeth in a socket will weaken. This would finally result in your teeth falling out.

Since teeth are very important, proper brushing (Fig. 14.4) and massage of gums are required everyday.

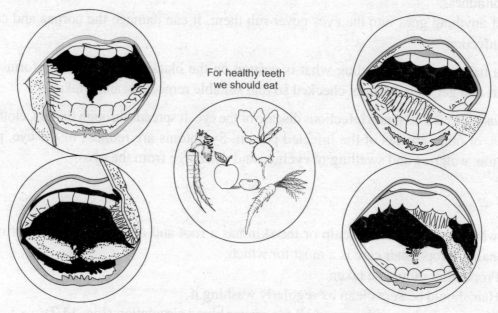

Fig. 14.4   Correct way of brushing the teeth

Eye Care

Eyes are one of the most important sense organs (Fig. 14.5). Proper cleanliness and care of the eyes is very essential. This can be done by following certain regular habits such as:

1. Eyes should be splashed with plenty of cold water every morning (Fig. 14.6).

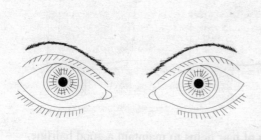

Fig. 14.5   One of the most important sense organs

Fig. 14.6   Wash your eyes regularly

2. While reading, a suitable distance of 25–30 cm of the eye from the book should be maintained.
3. Do not work in very dim or very bright light.
4. One should never read in a moving vehicle or while lying down.
5. Foods which are a rich source of vitamin A such as carrot, mango, tomato, cabbage, etc., should be included in the daily diet, as deficiency of vitamin A can cause night blindness.
6. If anything goes into the eyes never rub them. It can damage the cornea and cause infection.

If you have a problem reading what is written on the blackboard in class, inform your parents and get your eyesight checked so that suitable remedies can be taken.

Conjunctivitis is a common infectious disease of the eye. It spreads through fingers, clothing, towels, or other articles of the infected person. Symptoms are redness of the eye, pain, irritation, watering and swelling of eyelids, and discharge from the eyes.

Hair Care

Hair which arises from the scalp or the skin has a root and a stem. It is a part of one's personality. Proper hair care is a must for which:
1. Proper diet should be taken.
2. Hair should be kept clean by regularly washing it.
3. Massage the hair with a good oil for proper blood circulation (Fig. 14.7).

Fig. 14.7   Massaging, combing and brushing of hair helps to maintain a good hairline

4. Comb the hair regularly to increase blood circulation in the roots of hair. Each hair has an oil gland that produces natural oils. Combing/brushing helps to spread the oil evenly all over the hair.

5. Dandruff should be treated at the early stages itself as it causes premature hair fall.

6. Ensure there are no lice in the hair.

Recall

- Cleanliness of our body is very important.
- Teeth which are important for chewing of food and speaking have to be well-taken care of.
- Eyes are essential for proper vision. Good care should be taken for maintaining good eyesight.
- For healthy hair one should take a balanced diet.

Let's Answer

1. What is plaque? How does it result in the formation of a cavity in the tooth?
2. Suggest ways to prevent the formation of plaque.
3. Name an infectious disease of the eye. What are its symptoms?
4. The deficiency of which vitamin causes night blindness?
5. Why is it essential to wash your hair regularly?

COMMUNITY HYGIENE

Community hygiene includes:

1. Cleanliness of the surroundings.
2. Proper disposal of sewage.
3. Availability of germ-free drinking water.
4. Timely medical help.
5. Well-maintained spaces with lot of greenery.
6. Place for recreation.
7. Educating people to create social awareness about hygiene.

Personal hygiene can keep us healthy but community hygiene along with personal hygiene can make the environment healthy.

There are different aspects of community hygiene such as

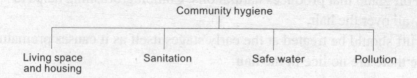

Community hygiene

Living space and housing   Sanitation   Safe water   Pollution

Living Space and Housing

With the increase in the population of our country, the land available for agriculture, industries and housing has reduced greatly. Job opportunities are drawing the rural population to the cities which is leading to unhygienic living conditions as the cities are becoming crowded. Water supply, electricity, drainage, etc.—every factor is affected and has to be upgraded regularly.

Sanitation

Disposal of waste which can be waste water from houses, human and animal excreta, and waste from factories and industries has to be managed so that they do not pollute the soil, water and the surroundings.

There are different methods to dispose off waste:

(a) **Dumping** In this method waste is deposited in pits in low-lying areas away from any agricultural land or water resources and populated areas. Waste is then covered with soil or sand after each dumping. The pit is completely covered after it gets filled up.

(b) **Burning** Sometimes, waste is mixed with dry leaves and twigs, and burnt. But this may cause pollution of the atmosphere.

(c) **Composting** Vegetable or agricultural waste, cow dung, animal waste, and human waste are put in pits or trenches. They are allowed to decompose. The waste gets converted into compost in a few months which can then be used as manure.

Safe Water

Water which is very essential for life should be (a) free from germs (b) free from chemicals and (c) good to taste.

Water containing micro-organisms can cause diseases such as diarrhoea or worms in the intestine. Chlorination of water helps in destroying the germs.

Storing water in earthen pots is also a healthy practice as sedimentation settles the impurities in water and at the same time evaporation cools the water.

Alum can also be added for purification of water.

Pollution

Man because of his need and greed has been misusing the various resources of the environment. For example, air has become unfit for respiration. Factories, cars, and industries discharge harmful poisonous gases which cause severe lung diseases and breathing problems.

Water pollution is another threat. Sewage, industrial waste, rain water carrying fertilizers and insecticides or pesticides pollute the water.

Soil gets polluted by the use of fertilizers, insecticides or pesticides. Even polythene and plastics pollute the soil.

Noise pollution is another threat to the modern world.

Some of the common health problems associated with pollution are headache, dizziness, fatigue, and hearing loss.

 Recall

- Community hygiene is as important as personal hygiene.
- Cleanliness is next to godliness.
- Proper disposal of human and animal waste is very important.
- Industrial waste should not be allowed to pollute the land, water and air.
- Pollution is a very big threat to our modern, progressive world and we need to take care of our environment by managing the waste thrown up by factories, industries, vehicles, fertilizers, and insecticides.
- Chlorination makes the water fit for drinking.

 Let's Answer

1. People living in a community need (a) a school (b) a hospital and (c) a park. Why do you think these are important?
2. State some measures which are essential for maintaining community hygiene.

PREVENTION OF COMMUNICABLE DISEASES

The disease that can get transmitted from one person to another is known as an infectious or communicable disease (Fig. 14.8). Mumps, malaria, tuberculosis, cough and cold, and hepatitis are some of the common communicable diseases.

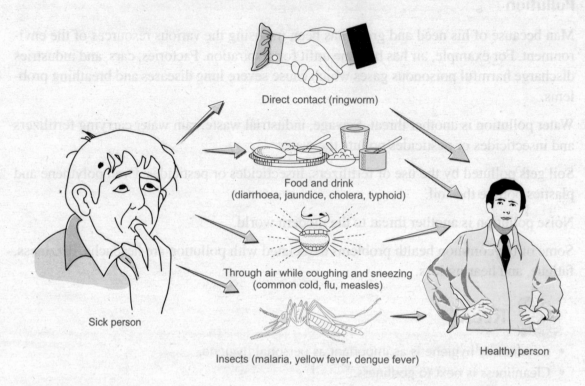

Fig. 14.8 Different ways in which germs can pass from a sick person to a healthy person

They can spread by
- certain insect bites.
- physical contact with an infected person or by sharing things such as bed, clothes, towel, etc.
- taking in of infected food or water.
- breathing in air containing micro-organisms.

To prevent these kind of infections take the following steps:
1. Drink filtered water.
2. Use mosquito nets or repellents.
3. Protect the food from flies.
4. Never use towels, clothes or utensils used by an infected person.
5. Cover your mouth with a handkerchief while sneezing or coughing.

Vaccination is an important method for preventing disease such as polio, cholera and hepatitis. The national immunization schedule in our country helps every child upto the age of 5 years to get vaccinated.

There are some diseases that are caused by our bad habits such as excessive consumption of alcohol, drugs, tobacco or smoking. Chewing of tobacco or smoking can cause lung cancer, while alcohol affects the liver. These habits affect both our physical and mental health.

 Recall

- Vaccination is a very effective method for preventing disease.
- The disease that can get transmitted from one person to another is known as an infectious or communicable disease.
- Diseases can also be caused by some bad habits such as consumption of alcohol, drugs, smoking, etc. These affect both our physical and mental health.

EXERCISES

1. **Choose the appropriate answer**

   (i) Chapati is a good source of
   - (a) fats
   - (b) proteins
   - (c) carbohydrates
   - (d) vitamins

   (ii) Which of the following can affect the rate of growth?
   - (a) Proteins
   - (b) Vitamins
   - (c) Minerals
   - (d) Fruits

   (iii) The proper method of disposal of vegetable and animal waste is
   - (a) putting it in an open pit
   - (b) putting it in a heap outside
   - (c) burning it in the open
   - (d) dumping it in water

   (iv) Health includes freedom from
   - (a) tension
   - (b) disease
   - (c) anxiety
   - (d) all of the above

   (v) Infectious diseases are caused by
   - (a) bacteria
   - (b) virus
   - (c) insect bite
   - (d) all of the above

   (vi) Conjunctivitis is a disease of
   - (a) teeth
   - (b) ears
   - (c) eyes
   - (d) hair

(vii) Which of these are communicable diseases?
- (a) Mumps
- (b) Malaria
- (c) Cough
- (d) All of the above

(viii) To avoid night blindness, we need to have food rich in
- (a) Vitamin A
- (b) Vitamin B
- (c) Vitamin C
- (d) Vitamin D

(ix) The hardest substance in our body is
- (a) the crown
- (b) the enamel
- (c) bone
- (d) the root

(x) Which of them is a genetic disease?
- (a) Cholera
- (b) Anaemia
- (c) Haemophilia
- (d) None of the above

2. Mark the following sentences as *True* or *False*
- (a) Never cover your face while sleeping.
- (b) Dandruff causes premature hair fall.
- (c) Rice contains proteins.
- (d) Deficiency of vitamin A causes obesity.
- (e) Spicy and fried food is not good for health.
- (f) Regular exercise is good for health.
- (g) Sweets and sticky food are not good for teeth.
- (h) Pulses contain carbohydrates.
- (i) Teeth give shape to our face and enable us to speak properly.
- (j) Vaccination is a preventive mechanism.

3. Match the following columns

A	B
(i) Vitamins	(a) Carbohydrate
(ii) Deficiency of iodine	(b) Teeth
(iii) Eyes	(c) Water
(iv) Plaque	(d) Protective food
(v) Vaccination	(e) Goitre
(vi) Chlorination	(f) Conjunctivitis
(vii) Proteins	(g) Polio
(viii) Rice	(h) Bodybuilding food

4. Give one word answers for the following
- (a) Vitamins and minerals are categorized as what kind of food?
- (b) Consumption of alcohol affects which organ of the body?
- (c) Which particular food has no nutrients but helps in regular bowel movement?
- (d) Which vegetable is a rich source of vitamin A?
- (e) Which food is rich in iodine?
- (f) What substance produced by bacteria in the mouth affects the enamel of the teeth?

(g) When waste gets converted into compost that can be used as manure, what is the process called?

(h) Name one disease spread by direct contact.

5. **Give reasons for the following**
   (a) City water supply should be chlorinated.
   (b) Stale food is bad for health.
   (c) Never read while travelling in a bus or a train.
   (d) Food should not be taken in a hurry.
   (e) Eating in a tension-free environment is good for health.

6. **Answer the following questions briefly**
   (a) Name the components of a balanced diet.
   (b) What is a balanced diet?
   (c) Why are vitamins and minerals called protective food?
   (d) Make a list of five factors that can affect your health.
   (e) What do you mean by the term personal hygiene?
   (f) Why do nails need to be trimmed regularly?
   (g) How can we take care of our eyes?
   (h) Why does hair need to be washed and combed regularly?
   (i) What is the importance of community health?
   (j) How can we turn garbage into manure?
   (k) Mention three important causes of tooth decay.
   (l) How can education be a tool for preventing disease?
   (m) What is a vaccine?
   (n) A friend of yours has developed a burning irritation in his eyes. They have turned red and watery. What is he suffering from and what advice will you give him?
   (o) Does working for long hours with the computer affect your eyes? If yes, how?

THINK AND ANSWER

1. In 1953 J.D. Watson and F.H.C. Crick discovered the structural arrangement of the DNA molecules.
   Today it is of great importance. Can you suggest why?
2. Superstitions do not help in maintaining good health. Why not?

 Teacher's Notes

- A visit can be made to the slum areas with the students to teach how hygiene is very important in our life.
- A spontaneous check on the lunch boxes of all the students can be made to find out who is carrying what kind of nutrients. This would definitely make the class interesting.

FAMOUS SCIENTISTS

Carolus Linnaeus (1707-1778)

Carl Linnaeus, also known as Carl von Linné or *Carolus Linnaeus,* is often called the *Father of Taxonomy.*

Linnaeus was the greatest botanist of the eighteenth century. In his *Systema Naturae* (1735), he established the classification of living things into genus and species, and combined related genera into classes, and related classes into orders. This system was more precise and useful than any previous one. Linnaeus's hierarchical classification and binomial nomenclature, much modified, have remained a standard for over 200 years.

Carolus Linnaeus

Louis Pasteur (1822-1895)

A world-renowned French chemist and biologist, *Louis Pasteur* was born in Dôle on December 27, 1822.

He proved the germ theory of disease, invented the process of pasteurization, and developed vaccines for several diseases, including rabies. He founded the *Institut Pasteur* in 1888 in Paris and this institute is today one of the most important centres in the world for the study of infectious diseases, and other subjects related to micro-organisms, including molecular genetics.

Louis Pasteur

Anders Celsius (1701-1744)

Anders Celsius was born in Uppsala, Sweden in 1701, where he succeeded his father as professor of astronomy in 1730. It was there that he built Sweden's first observatory in 1741, the Uppsala Observatory, where he was appointed director. He devised the centigrade scale or *Celsius scale* of temperature in 1742. Centigrade means *consisting of or divided into 100 degrees.*

Celsius was also an inventor and astronomer, in addition to being a physicist.

Anders Celsius

Lord Kelvin (1824-1907)

Lord Kelvin, who was born *William Thomson* on June 26, 1824 in Belfast, Ireland, invented the *Kelvin scale* for measuring temperatures in 1848.

The size of one unit is the same as the size of one degree Celsius. Water freezes at 273.16 K and boils at 373.16 K. Among his other achievements are the 1852 discovery of the Joule-Thomson Effect of gases and his work on the first transatlantic telegraph cable.

Lord Kelvin

Joseph Priestley (1733–1804)

Joseph Priestley was an English presbyterian minister and chemist. He was a pioneer in the chemistry of gases, and one of the discoverers of oxygen. He met Benjamin Franklin who supplied him with books which assisted him in the writing of, in 1767, *The History of Electricity*.

Joseph Priestley

Evangelista Torricelli (1608–47)

Evangelista Torricelli will always be known for the invention of the *Torricellian tube*. It was on account of Torricelli's experiments that we have come to better understand the nature of atmospheric pressure. For example, it was Torricelli who first found out that water will not rise above 33 feet in a suction pump.

Evangelista Torricelli

Galileo Galilei (1564–1642)

Galileo studied at Pisa, where he later held the chair in mathematics from 1589 to 1592. He invented the microscope, and built a telescope with which he observed objects in the sky, the most spectacular of which was his discovery of the satellites of Jupiter. He also studied Saturn and observed the phases of Venus.

He was heavily opposed by the Church for supporting Copernicus' theory that the earth and the other planets revolved around the sun. Till then it was believed that the earth was the centre of the universe and that the moon, the stars, the sun and the planets moved around the earth.

Galileo Galilei

Isaac Newton (1642–1727)

Newton was an English physicist and mathematician born into a poor farming family. Luckily for humanity, Newton was not a good farmer, and so was sent to Cambridge to study.

Newton is best known for his three laws of motion. Between August 1684 and the spring of 1686 he worked on the mathematics of orbits, and the result became one of the most important and influential works on physics of all times, *The Principia*.

Isaac Newton

Joseph Priestley

Evangelista Torricelli

Galileo Galilei

Isaac Newton

Joseph Priestley (1733–1804)

Joseph Priestley was an English-speaking theologian minister and chemist. He was a pioneer in the chemistry of gases, and one of the discoverers of oxygen. He met Benjamin Franklin who supplied him with books, which assisted him in the writing of his (1767) *History of Electricity*.

Evangelista Torricelli (1608–47)

Evangelista Torricelli will always be known for the invention of the Torricellian tube. It was a measurement of Torricelli's experiment that we begin soon to understand the nature of atmospheric pressure. For example, it was Torricelli who first found out that vacuum occurs above 33 feet in a suction pump.

Galileo Galilei (1564–1642)

Galileo studied at Pisa, where he taught for a while in mathematics from 1589 to 1592. He invented the microscope, and built a telescope with which he observed bodies in the sky. By that same telescope in which a real discovery of the satellites of Jupiter. He also studied Saturn and observed the phases of Venus.

He was largely opposed to the Church's teaching. He put forward the theory that the earth and the other planets travelled around the sun. Till then it was believed that the earth was the centre of the universe and that the moon, the stars, the sun and the planets moved around the earth.

Isaac Newton (1642–1727)

Newton was an English physicist and mathematician born into a poor farming family. Luckily for humanity Newton was not a good farmer, and so was sent to university to study.

Newton is best known for the three laws of motion, his work with light and the `prism' of each. He worked on the mathematics of orbits, and the result became one of the most important and influential works on physics of all time. The *Principia*.

246